SON OF RAVEN, SON OF DEER

Fables of the Tse-shaht People

George Clutesi

'SON OF RAVEN
SON OF DEER,

Illustrations by the Author

Clutesi Agencies Limited
Port Alberni, British Columbia, Canada

Copyright © 1967 George C. Clutesi
First Printing, June 1967
Second Printing, September 1967
Second Edition, April 1968

Copyright © 1994 Clutesi Agencies Limited
Third Edition, October 1994

Son of Raven, Son of Deer is published by
Clutesi Agencies Limited.

Printed in Canada

Canadian Cataloguing in Publication Data

Clutesi, George, 1905-1988.
  Son of raven, son of deer

ISBN 0-9698677-0-1

  1. Nootka Indians -- Folklore. 2. Indians of North America--
British Columbia--Folklore. I. Title.

E99.N85C4 1994   398.2'09711   C94-910918-5

Dedication

This book I dedicate to my wife Margaret, who urged
me to recall these fables of my people, and to our six
children who loved them all.

CLUTESI, 1967

Contents

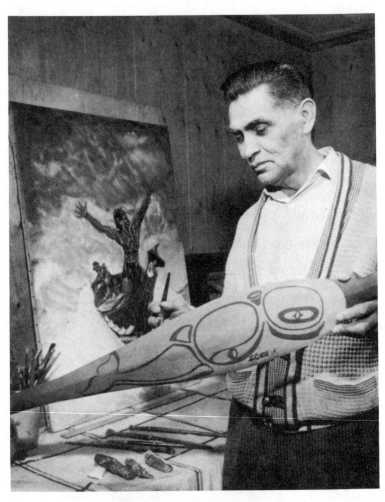

The Author and Illustrator
PHOTO BY DANE CAMPBELL

Introduction

This series of Indian folklore tales will not be just another attempt to portray the past and the sometimes romantic aspects of a nearly forgotten culture of a once carefree, happy, singing people. Instead, it will be an attempt to approach from the back door, as it were, to an apparently rich and cultured society. The series will endeavour to reach the more sensitive, the more sympathetic and the more reasoning segment of the non-Indians, who may have some willingness to study and understand the culture of the true Indian, whose mind was imaginative, romantic and resourceful.

My father's generation was a happy, singing people. They were a proud people. They were a strong and healthy people. They knew what they wanted and what was good for their own. The Indian aspired to a clean and wholesome mind and a staunch, fearless heart. He was at peace with his god and he was at peace with himself.

Quaint folklore tales were used widely to teach the young the many wonders of nature; the importance of all living things, no matter how small and insignificant; and particularly to acquaint him with the closeness of man to all animal, bird life and the creatures of the sea. The young were taught through the medium of the tales that there was a place in the sun for all living things.

This resulted in a deep understanding and love of man for all animal life. This was so prevalent that an Indian would show remorse and do penance on the spot whenever he even killed an animal for meat. This practise prevailed throughout all the coastal region of British Columbia.

The Indian parent refrained from the non-Indian adage of "Don't do this. Don't do that." Instead he taught his children in parables and tales in which all animals in his own world played important roles. It was not long before the child realized that all animal life was an integral part of all creation.

The West Coast Indian had many tales of this nature. The following examples will be like a minute drop of sparkling dew that, perchance, may have rolled down the stem of a swaying reed into the cupped and gnarled hands of "Nan-is," a grandparent, who loved to tell them to his "Ka-coots," grandchildren.

Nan-is had lived a full life. He had long since fulfilled the mission his creator may have allotted to him. He had aspired for and reached goals set by his own father's teachings and tenets. he may have begun as an average hunter; in his time he reached the pinnacle of being a foremost hunter. He was never quite content with his own prowess.

Nan-is was old now. His hunting days were nothing more than pleasant memories that often lifted his sometimes waning spirits. In spite of his great age Nan-is was still a very important member of his society. He was the story-teller to all his ka-coots. Moreover, he was loved and respected, understood by all because of his great patience with the young and his great love for them was very evident in his voice and speech. The young understood his tales and gained great benefit from the morals contained in them.

The Indian child of today is left bewildered by the white man's fairy tales that are too often tragic, injurious and harmful and frequently foster anxiety in the childish mind.

Some classical examples of this type of fairy tale can be found in the rhyme, Rock-a-bye baby in the tree top, When the wind blows the cradle will rock, When the bough breaks the cradle will fall, And down will come baby, cradle and all. – Jack and Jill went up the hill to get a pail of water, Jack fell down and broke his crown, and Jill came tumbling after. – Humpty Dumpty sat on a wall, Humpty Dumpty had a great fall, All the King's horses and the King's men couldn't put Humpty Dumpty together again. – London Bridge is falling down. – Henny Penny's loud proclamation to all that the sky was falling. – Little Jack Horner sat in a corner eating a Christmas pie. He put in his thumb and pulled out a plum and said what a good boy am I.

The Indian child feels bewilderment with this type of nursery rhyme because there seems to be no concern or regard for a very apparent injury inflicted upon a little child – which, in his own world, may very well be himself. He may reason also, why go to the top of a hill to get water when in his world all water is found at the bottom of hills.

To his immature mind the same message is found
in the classical lullaby. To him there cannot be joy in
the fact a bough broke and little baby came tumbling down. Humpty Dumpty to him is a living
thing who got smashed up in a fall and could not be
mended. London Bridge, a great structure, comes
crashing down which will create in him a sense of
insecurity - as will the sky when it falls. When he is
bad the teacher sends him to a corner. If he so much
as thinks of messing about with a gooey pie he is a
bad boy - not a good one, as the tale implies Jack
Horner was.

I have used these tales as examples because they
belong to the white man's classic nursery stories.
The Indian child is prone to accept these as folklore
stories of the white man, and therefore the truth,
since he is no longer able to hear many of his own
people's folklore tales. This could be part of the reason so many of the Indian population of Canada
are in a state of bewilderment today.

It is true he is taught in the same schools as the
non-Indian. But in spite of his new access to education, in spite of all the stepped-up efforts put
forth to "civilize" him, he shows little inclination to
make use of that type of education.

He cannot see why he must go up a hill to get a
pail of water; why there is no concern about a baby
falling from a tree; the tragic fate of Humpty Dumpty; why Jack Horner can be such a good boy, when
he, the Indian, is punished in his home for such
tricks.

Thus there is bewilderment in the average Canadian Indian. There is, in fact, a broken link in his life-growing period.

This process came about during the attempt to educate him overnight, as it were; he is, or was, constantly told to "do," but never "why." He was always led, but never shown where. He was taught to always turn the other cheek when accosted, only to be knocked down; and when prostrate his erstwhile benefactors turned the other way, and perhaps whispered – "he is full of shame."

What then can be done to really help the Indian at this time? One way would be to look for his better qualities. He has some. Meet him halfway. Try harder to become a sincere friend. You cannot fool an Indian with the gushing displays of hypocritical prying of a would-be do-gooder. Once his confidence is won he will show himself to be a lifelong friend.

Like other ancient races, the Indians believed in the magical powers of numbers. His was number four. In all his ceremonial procedures, customs, actions and teaching the number four was invariably used to denote the completeness of any task, enterprise or song; for four days and four nights he prepared himself physically and morally to communicate with his god. His song was always sung four times; so too was the main point of a lesson for a child so he may discover and perceive on his own, thus remember and benefit to the fullest possible extent, the morals therein. The number four was, of course, used in other areas as well.

This may explain the recurring phrases often seen in true Indian stories. Finally, when an Indian, be he child or adult, hears a song, a story, a legend a folklore tale or a phrase the full four times, he is expected to have grasped the main tune or theme.

Now let us explore together some of the tales that made the first peoples of this beautiful land a happy, singing people.

GEORGE C. CLUTESI

SON OF RAVEN, SON OF DEER

"I'll get you the fire."

How the Human People Got the First Fire

Long, long time ago the human people had no fire.
There was no fire to cook the food,
The people ate their food cold.
There was no fire to dry their clothes,
No fire to warm them at winter time.
There was no fire to give them light when the moon
would not.

It has been said there was no fire at all amongst the human people. No one had fire, except the Wolf people.

The Wolf people were the most dreaded people in all the land.

"No other people shall ever have our fire," they would say, and they guarded it with care, for they alone owned the precious fire.

"No one shall have it," they declared.

The human people wanted and needed the fire very much. Great chiefs and their wise councillors would sit and make plans, and more plans to find a way in which to capture the wondrous fire.

"Let us call all the strong and brave men," the wise men would say.

So the great chiefs from all the land would command that all men come forward and try to capture the fire. The strongest would boast that he would go forth to the land of the Wolf people and force his way into their village and bring the fire back. He was strong. The brave knew no fear. He would go forth and capture the fire.

The wise one would say, "I will find a way to win the fire. I am wise."

The fastest would boast, "I will run off with the fire and bring it here to you all. I am fast."

One by one they would go out to capture the fire, and one by one they would come back with the same story. It cannot be done!

The strongest would say, "I could not even get near the village of the dreadful Wolves. They have guards all over the place of the fire. No one can ever enter their village. We can never have the fire. The Wolves are too smart for us.

The fastest would say, "I got so close to their village that I could smell the food roasting in their great fires, but I could not enter their great house."

The wise old one would say, "I'll think of a way."

The great chief was very sad. His best men had failed him and all the people of the land.

"What shall we do? What can we do? We shall be cold again this winter. We shall again eat cold, raw food. We shall be blind by night when the moon will not give us light, and there is no fire to light the way. We must have the fire! We must!" cried the great chief in despair.

No one spoke. No one moved. All eyes were cast down. All had tried and all had failed. All the people were very sad indeed.

All throughout the great struggle for the possession of the fire Ah-tush-mit had been gambolling about the beach, racing, leaping and hopping about on his long spindly legs. He had seemingly paid no heed to all the great fuss about the fire.

He was racing past the people, as he had done so many times before, when suddenly he stopped directly in front of the chief and announced very simply in a small, small voice, "I'll get you the fire."

"You will what? What did that little boy say?" There was anger in the loud queries from the great braves and the strong men.

Then from the foolhardy ones a loud hee-haw went up — "Ho-ho-ho-ho-ho-ho."

"I'll get you the fire," the small boy repeated quite unabashed and not a bit frightened of the braves and the strong men, for he knew they had all tried and had failed to capture the fire.

Looking the great chief full in the face, Ah-tush-mit repeated again, "I'll get you the fire."

The little boy stood there, so small, so tiny and foolish looking among the great strong men. The wise chief was solemn while the others chuckled and laughed.

Ah-tush-mit, the Son of Deer, began twitching his long, long ears and rolling his big eyes as he looked this way and that way — but still he held his ground.

"I'll get you the fire," he persisted.

At last the great chief looked up and said, "Choo — all right — Ah-tush-mit, my strongest, bravest, fastest and wisest have all failed. Do the best you can."

Ah-tush-mit called the womenfolk together.

"Make me the most colourful costume you can," he commanded. "I am going to dance for the great Wolf chief."

"Dance? Who wants to dance at a time like this?" all the women wanted to know. "The boy is really foolish. He is wasting our time," they all declared.

"Obey and do everything Ah-tush-mit says," the wise old chief commanded his people. "Let the boy try. Give him a chance as I did to all of you," he continued.

Thus the womenfolk made him a head-band, a sash for his belt, bands for his knees and elbows, and for his ankles too. All these were made from the inner bark of the cedar tree, and dyed the colour of the young cohoe salmon — as red as red can be.

Ah-tush-mit fitted and worked with his regalia until it was just right. He paid special attention to the bands for his knees. He kept remarking these kneebands had to fit exactly right — not too tight, not too loose — just right so that he could dance well for the great Wolves.

While he was paying special attention to the knee-bands no one noticed that he tucked something into them between the bark and his skin. He worked with the knee-bands and finally they were smooth and exactly to his liking.

"Now I want the best drummers and singers," he announced. "Come with me to the outskirts of the Wolf village. Do not enter with me. When I give the signal you must all run back home as fast as you can."

"We shall go before dark so that you can reach your homes before the night blinds you," he assured the brave men and women drummers and singers who were to risk their very lives to accompany him to the outskirts of the Wolf village.

At last everything was in readiness. Evening came. Ah-tush-mit sallied forth to capture the fire for the human people from the most dreaded people in the land, the Wolf people.

"Show yourselves. Do not hide or sneak in any manner," he warned. "The Wolf people are wise and cunning. They would be sure to see us anyway, even if we were to try and sneak in by the dark of the night."

So the odd little company sang and beat their drums with all their might and main. The Wolf people heard them from a long distance off they sang so lustily. One strange thing took place. Ah-tush-mit did not take the lead as everyone had expected. Instead he hid himself behind the company of drummers.

"Ah, the foolish boy is now too frightened to show himself?" the women asked one another.

Finally the group of singers and drummers reached the outskirts of the great village of the dreaded Wolves. The huge doors of the house opened slowly, and the biggest, fiercest-looking Wolves bounded out to see what all the noise and din was about.

The humans could see the large fire burning and blazing inside the great house of the Wolves. They could almost feel the heat and the smoke smelled so sweet as they inhaled with all their might, for they had never before seen or smelled the fire.

What a wondrous beautiful sight! Great sparks burst and escaped through the smoke hole on the top of the great roof. What a wonderful thing! So bright and beautiful in the gathering gloom of the dark night. These were the thoughts that ran through the minds of the awe-stricken humans.

Suddenly Ah-tush-mit sprang forward from his place of concealment. He was on all fours as he began his dance. He sidled towards the door of the great Wolf house. It was fast getting dark. The flickering light from the fire reached out to him and cast pleasing shadows all around as he danced and sprang about on his four spindly legs. Suddenly, he made the signal and the singers and drummers stopped their din abruptly and fled for home as they had been instructed.

Little Ah-tush-mit was left all alone with the fire and the fierce Wolves. There were no more drums nor singers to give him courage, and he was very frightened. He was very, very frightened indeed.

He could hear the Wolf chief asking, "What is all the noise about?"

A Wolf guard answered, "It is only young Ah-tush-mit dancing."

"Send him away," the chief growled.

"Ah, what a jolly little boy! Bring him in. Do let him in," the Wolf chief's wife called out.

"Let us see him dance for awhile, then send him home," the chief agreed.

Ah-tush-mit increased the pace of his dance. Towards the great doors he pranced, hopping straight up and down, with no bend to his knees. Hop, hop, hop, hop, he went, sidling ever closer to the opening of the doorway, and as he circled around he sang a rollicking ditty.

Kiyaaa tlin, tlin, tlin, tlin,
Kiyaaa tlin, tlin, tlin, tlin,
Ooo nootl sahshh keeyah-qwa-yup qwatlin,
Hee yah ahh haaa ya-yaulk tah khaus ti-nah-is,
Kiyaaa tlin, tlin, tlin, tlin,
Kiyaaa, tlin, tlin, tlin, tlin.

Break, crack, crack, crack, crack,
Break, crack, crack, crack, crack,
Do I break yon stakes with these I wear?
My flints, my sandstone hooves,
Break, crack, crack, crack, crack,
Break, crack, crack, crack, crack.

Over the fire sailed he

Ah-tush-mit's voice was small, but he sang with all his heart. He sang with all his might. He was singing to capture a spark. Ah-tush-mit was singing for his life!

Hop, hop, hop, hop, stiff-legged, he entered the doors. Once inside he could see the fire burning brightly and all about it was a bed of stakes made of broken bones implanted into the earth, as sharp as mussel shells they were. This was what his little song was all about. Up to this very minute no human who had ever tried to get past that awful bed of bone stakes had lived to tell the tale.

Ah-tush-mit danced with all his heart. He danced as he had never danced before. He danced so he might capture a tiny spark. Ah-tush-mit danced for his life.

"Kiyaaa tlin, tlin, tlin, tlin," he sang as he sidled ever closer towards the awful trap made with broken bones. Skirting its edges in a half circle, he danced towards a far corner, closer to the fire, but where the bones were neither so large nor too plentiful in the ground.

Suddenly he had arrived at his chosen spot and with a mighty leap he was among the broken bones, hopping higher and ever higher as he picked his way among the sharp spear-like bones. His sharp little feet seemed to fit around and pass between the dangerous bones harmlessly. His long shanks and slim legs kept his plump little body safely away from the sharp, sharp points and thus he was saved from being torn to shreds.

"Do I break yon stakes of bones with these I wear? My flints, my sandstone hooves?" he sang.

The Wolf people were completely fascinated. Their big and awful jaws hung open in wonderment. Ah-tush-mit had won the cheer and applause of the Wolf people.

The little fellow's bright costume glowed in the firelight.

"Break, crack, crack, crack, crack," his little song floated over the great fire. "With these I wear my flints, my sandstone hooves," he carolled as he suddenly sprang right beside the great fire.

Ah-tush-mit sang louder and louder; he leaped higher and ever higher; he was dancing to capture a spark; he was dancing for his very life.

"Ah, what a jolly little boy! He is a dancer, a good dancer," the mamma Wolf beamed.

Then it happened — as quick as a flash — before your eyes could blink. Ah-tush-mit had turned towards the roaring fire and with a mighty leap he sailed into the air — right over the roaring fire sailed he.

"Ho-ho-ho-ho-ho," roared the Wolves "Ah-tush-mit is on fire. Ho-ho-ho-ho-ho."

Ah-tush-mit had indeed caught on fire. His little legs smouldered between the knees. He stopped his dancing and bounded through the great doors with a mighty leap. Once clear of the great Wolf house he raced for his life towards home as fast as he could run.

All around the leaping, roaring fire the Wolves sat bemused. The whole action of little Ah-tush-mit had happened so quickly and seemingly without intent that they were taken completely by surprise. Before they realized what had occurred Ah-tush-mit was well away from the Wolf village. Ah-tush-mit, the Son of Deer, the fleetest of them all, had completely out-smarted the Wolves, the most dreaded people of the land.

With a spark smouldering between his knees he had captured the fire! With his sharp pointed feet, his flints and sandstone hooves he had successfully run the sharp broken stakes of bones.

Yes indeed, with his colourful costume, his captivating dance, he had outwitted the most cunning people of the land. Ah-tush-mit, Son of Deer, the small one, had captured the fire for the human people.

The secret something Ah-tush-mit had tucked between his knees had been a small bundle of very dry sticks he had gathered from the undermost branches of the spruce tree. It was this that had caught fire since it was dry as dry can be, and even some of the spruce gum still stuck to the twigs. When the sticks caught fire the cedar bark bands had smouldered until he reached home with the tiny sparks of fire. This was where the tinder had come from and where the human people first came to know about fire.

But Ah-tush-mit had burned himself. The inside of his knees were badly scorched. Thus it is to this day that the inside of all deers' knees are singed black. That is how the human people got their first fire.

In the growing season, when all living things
*   burst out in bloom*
Sit in the glade of the wood at even-tide.
If your own heart be open to love be there for Ah-tush-mit
you will hear the thump and the beat of his little song:
Thump, thump, thump, thump.

Ko-ishin-mit and his herring rake

Ko-ishin-mit Goes Fishing

Cloosmit the herring, hosts in the night.
The flash of silver, the flame of your gold,
With the grey of the dawn you are gone.
Cloosmit the herring, the shoal of the sea,
Come! Dance upon the waters in a sea of spray.
Come! Feed the children of the land with your spawn

Cloosmit the herring, hosts in the night.
The flash of silver, the flame of your gold.
Come! Make thunder upon the waters in the bay.
With your hosts make thunder in a sea of spray.
Come! Dance upon the waters with the dawn.
Come! Feed the children of the land with your spawn.

Gusty winds were here. The sun would come out bright and bold; the cloud, black with anger, would roll and push it out of sight. The rain and snow would make the sleet cold with fury, and the winds would push them all away. The sun would shine again. The Moon of many Moods was here.

It was early spring. The growing, budding season had come; the herring, in great shoals, were coming into the bay to get ready for the huge spawn. The fish would come swarming into the bay in great schools. In the morning with the break of day and the dusk of the evening the herring would come up and play upon the surface of the waters, or swish across the bay like a roll of thunder in a sea of spray.

The Indian people were busy fishing for the herring. The fishermen would stand on the bows of their canoes, and with their long, long rakes poised high in the air, they would push them slowly into the depths of the waters, cutting into the schools of herring as they raked the wiggling, silvery fish into their canoes. The good fishermen would soon fill their craft with the herring that shimmered in the early sun, and as they beached their laden craft the people would come down to the shore and take all they needed. The Indian people always loved to share their foodstuffs with their neighbours.

Ko-ishin-mit liked to watch the fishermen come in with the fresh herring still wiggling and flipping about, some even managing to leap over the side and so escape back to sea again. The sleek, colourful bodies, at one moment all silver, the next changing to the colours of Tsa-wah-youse, the rainbow. Then best of all Ko-ishin-mit loved to fill his biggest basket with the beautiful fish to take home to his little wife, Pash-hook, who would then smoke and dry the fish for summer use. Pash-hook was a dutiful wife. It was said that Pash-hook was light minded and very forgetful. This is why she was named Pash-hook, which means exactly that. Pash-hook was the daughter of Dsim-do the squirrel. She was always trying her best to please her husband Ko-ishin-mit.

One morning Ko-ishin-mit, the young Son of Raven, asked the best fisherman, the man who brought in the most herring every morning, why he used such long poles for his rake.

"Why is your rake handle extra long?" he wanted to know.

"I will tell you, Son of Raven, if you promise never to tell it to anyone else," the man whispered. "This is a secret of mine that no one knows. The longer the pole, the wider the rake I can use. The wider the rake the more herring get caught with it. It is very easy. Take your pole, poke it down very carefully into the water until it is straight up and down beside your chapahts, your canoe. Then you must push it down into the depths with all your might so it will go deep where the herring lurk. Then you must peer over the side to watch for it to come swishing back to you full of fish. It's that easy. Remember the harder you push the deeper it will sink and the more fish will stick on it." The man spoke in a whisper, and very seriously asked Ko-ishin-mit never to give the secret away now that he too knew the secret as well.

"That is how I catch the most herring," the man said as he walked away.

Ko-ishin-mit sat all through this long explanation in goggle-eyed concern. He took in every word the man had told him.

The next day Ko-ishin-mit was seen making an extra-long pole and a very wide rake. "I am going for herring," he told everyone that passed by. He assured his little wife Pash-hook that she would soon have all the herring she could possibly smoke.

At last the rake was finished. It was long. It was wide. It was big. Pash-hook beamed as she watched her dear husband trim and polish the rake handle and sharpen the barbs with loving care. Pash-hook loved her husband very much and was always trying hard to please him.

It was still very dark. The moon was not there. All the fishermen were still fast asleep. Ko-ishin-mit was up and busy with his new fishing gear. He pulled his cha-pahts, little canoe, down to the water; he carried his long rake next and placed it carefully in the canoe. It was extra wide; it was too long, but Ko-ishin-mit did not care. This was his new secret, he boasted.

Ko-ishin-mit paddled around the bay; he paddled across the bay; he paddled everywhere. Every now and then he would put his little paddle down and peer into the darkness, listening, listening for the flip of the herring.

There was no herring! No fish flipped upon the surface of the waters. It was awfully dark. The moon was not there. It was still night. Ko-ishin-mit did not care. He knew the secret. He listened again. He would find fish, he was sure. He would fill his cha-pahts full of the fattest herring, he boasted to himself.

He would land his cha-pahts in front of the village with the herring spilling over the sides. Then he would call with all his might — "Ho-ooooooooo come and receive your herring. Ho-ooooooo come and receive your herring." He would be a hero. He would be the best fisherman, he smiled to himself.

Ko-ishin-mit stopped at a place he knew was very deep. He carefully lifted his long, long rake. It was very heavy and his little cha-pahts wobbled and threatened to turn over. Carefully he got the long pole to stand straight up and down, as the man had said, and he poked it down deep, pushing it down with all his strength. Straight down he pushed his herring rake — down, down it went until it disappeared in the dark waters.

As the pole went out of sight Ko-ishin-mit leaned down over the side of his canoe to watch the rake come up laden with big, fat herring. He would soon have his cha-pahts full. He would soon be a hero, the best fisherman.

So intent was Ko-ishin-mit on his thought that he didn't see the pole bounce suddenly out of the water. It came back with a mighty surge and — Wham! it smacked poor Ko-ishin-mit right on his nose. He was thrown backwards into his canoe and lay still. One instant he had been looking for the pole to come up — the next there was a sea of bright stars dancing all around his head. When he came to, that was all he remembered. Poor Ko-ishin-mit! His nose swelled and swelled and it was long and black.

The people found him lying in his canoe as it drifted in the bay. They towed him home and Pash-hook put him to bed. There was no herring; there was just a very hurt and very sick Ko-ishin-mit.

When you push a pole into the water it shoots back up like a spear. It is very dangerous. Ko-ishin-mit discovered this too late. The man had not told him this because he was always copying other people.

It is said that children should not always believe other people. Sometimes they tell things that are not true.

Raven the rook, would a herring to rake.
Down to the waters, a herring to take,
Down into the deep, he pushed his rake,
Down into the depths, to see it come back.
Up it came, smack upon his nose it came back
And it swelled and swelled to a big black nose.

Ah-tush-mit burns his hopinwush.

Ah-tush-mit Burns His Canoe

Ah-tush-mit was a curious and inquisitive little boy. He would stop to stare and to admire almost anything that he saw, with his great big eyes filled with wonder and amazement. If he heard a noise he would investigate to see what had made the noise. If he saw something unusual, his eyes would grow big with pure delight. How Ah-tush-mit loved to stand and stare!

One day young Ah-tush-mit decided to burn and polish the underside of his little hopinwush, dugout, so that it would go faster in the water. He went down to the beach to gather some dry cedar to make the faggot. This was a bundle of dry sticks that he would light and move carefully along the underside of his precious little canoe to scorch off the fuzz that had grown and leave it smooth and polished.

"You have to be very careful and you have to know just how to do this, or else you might burn your canoe," Ah-tush-mit boastfully sang.

All the morning he worked hard at splitting the cedar, chopping it into the right length with his little stone hatchet and mussel-shell knife. And all the while he worked he sang joyfully — "You have to be careful or else you will burn your canoe."

At last he had enough faggots made. He carefully tied the sticks into a neat bundle and hoisting them to his shoulders, toted them to where his little hopinwush was beached.

He pulled and hauled the canoe up onto a log and turned it upside down ready for the big job. This was very hard work for Ah-tush-mit because he was very small with skinny little legs and arms.

As soon as the hopinwush was lying just right he very carefully brushed off all the sand with his canoe mat. This mat was made from the stalks of bullrushes. It was very soft. Ah-tush-mit decided the inside of the canoe needed a cleaning too so he turned it over and cleansed it thoroughly. He was going to do the job right, he boasted.

One of the village braves was watching intently while Ah-tush-mit was hard at work with his little canoe. There was a mischievous grin on the man's handsome face. He looked around and saw some of the other menfolk of the village were nearby, also busy working on their own canoes.

"Ah-tush-mit, the inquisitive one," the man with the merry smile on his face announced loudly enough so that all nearby could hear him, "is going to burn and polish his little hopinwush."

All the men stopped their work and waited for what they sensed would follow, for this man with the merry voice was well known for his pranks. He loved playing tricks on unsuspecting people of the village.

"Come, you menfolk, come and watch Ah-tush-mit burn and polish his little hopinwush," he repeated as he vanished into a nearby clump of bushes. The braves gathered around the little canoe to watch.

Ah-tush-mit felt very important because of all the attention he was getting from the grown men of the village. "I'll show these men I can do my own work now," he boasted to himself.

Ah-tush-mit was half-way down his canoe with the burning. He had been extra careful with the blazing faggot. "I must keep the faggot moving all the time," he kept reminding himself. "Keep it moving. Keep it moving. I must not burn my little hopinwush," he sang. Ah-tush-mit loved to sing and he made songs of every little thing he did. "No, no, I must not burn my hopinwush small. Oh— he was so careful!"

In a short time the wind began to blow the smoke into his eyes. His little round forehead got burned and was singed black with smoke. His little nose was entirely blackened with soot. His own perspiration rolled down his forehead and into his eyes, making them watery until he could hardly see.

"This is hard work. This is too hard," he admitted to himself, as he shook his little head to get rid of the water in his eyes. "This is too —" he began to say when he remembered that the village menfolk were standing nearby watching and admiring his work — so he began to sing again — "I must not, I must not burn my hopinwush."

Suddenly it came to Ah-tush-mit that he might be on the wrong side of the wind. He moved over to the other side, and immediately the wind blew the smoke away from him. "Ah, this is better," he thought, as he resumed his singing — "I'll make my canoe, my hopinwush, the fastest in the whole village."

Suddenly, from a nearby clump of bushes beside where Ah-tush-mit, the inquisitive one, was toiling so hard, there floated up a lone vibrant voice. It was a singing voice, singing a dancing song. It came floating in with the soft morning breeze of the early spring. It was a beautiful song.

Presently a man with a sprig of hemlock branches tied atop his head, and with arms set akimbo, sprang from the nearby clump of bushes. He sang lustily as he began to dance down the sandy beach. The man danced harder as his voice grew stronger. The man danced with all his might.

Ah-tush-mit stood absolutely spellbound. He stood perfectly still, his big eyes wide with wonder, as the dancer moved down the white sandy beach.

"I wish I could dance like that," Ah-tush-mit thought to himself. "I wish I could dance like that."

All the people of the village had gathered along the beach to watch the fun when they heard the vibrant voice come floating over the village. But, alas, they were not watching the dancer. They were watching little Ah-tush-mit, the inquisitive one.

Ah-tush-mit had completely forgotten his work
at hand. He had not once moved his blazing faggot
after the dancer appeared. It stayed at the very
middle of his hopinwush — burning — burning —
burning.... The blazing faggot had burned the precious little canoe right in two.

Crash! The hopinwush fell from the log where
Ah-tush-mit had so laboriously placed it. Crash! It
burned apart in the middle.

"Ah-hhhhhhhh," wailed the assembled womenfolk.

"Tu-shack?" — "What has happened?" wailed poor
Ah-tush-mit, the inquisitive one.

Ah-tush-mit went home very sad indeed because
he had burned his own hopinwush. His forehead
was singed black and his little nose blackened with
soot.

The prankster went home, chuckling to himself.

"Seek, seek, seek."

Ko-ishin-mit and
Son of Eagle

Ko-ishin-mit loved to copy and imitate other people — especially the clever people. He would watch them doing their tasks, then he would go home and imitate them, no matter how hard it might be. He loved to go around visiting his neighbours at mealtime, looking for free meals. He would walk for miles for a feed. Oh, how Ko-ishin-mit loved to eat! Ko-ishin-mit would eat anything put before him, he was so greedy.

One fine, lovely morning in the spring of the year Ko-ishin-mit was sitting by the river. He watched the beautiful swallows as they swooped and skimmed the surface of the water while they picked up flies and insects. The swiftly-flying birds would sometimes come so close over his head that he would fall backwards as he followed their flight.

All of a sudden, and very near to where he sat, a salmon broke the calm surface of the pool. It was a very large hissit, sockeye salmon. Ko-ishin-mit was on his feet in an instant and peering into the pool. To his great excitement he saw that there was a school of salmon passing. They were swimming with ease up the lazy river.

"Oh, how I wish I could have sockeye salmon for my dinner," he drooled.

Ko-ishin-mit knew very well that he couldn't catch one. He hopped along the bank following the school of salmon.

"How can I? I know. I know — I'll go and visit Son of Eagle. Yes! I'll visit Son of Eagle. He always has fresh salmon for dinner."

Son of Eagle lived very far away. His house was far, far down the river. He lived at the mouth of the river but Ko-ishin-mit did not mind that at all. Without waiting to see more salmon, Ko-ishin-mit started down the river. He walked and he walked. After a long, long time he sensed the smell of salt in the air. He knew the Eagle's house was near the sea. At last he reached the place. There was the house. How hungry he was! He had walked far.

Near to the house was a tall, tall tree. Its topmost branch seemed to reach to the blue sky above. On this tall tree Son of Eagle loved to sit and watch for the salmon as they went upstream. The sly Ko-ishin-mit pretended to be passing by. He knew very well he would be invited in because he was so far from his own home. So he sauntered by the house humming a song just in case Son of Eagle should miss seeing him. He was very, very hungry by this time.

All of the people, he well knew, had been taught never to let anyone, whoever he might be, pass without inviting him in for a meal. Son of Eagle was said to be among the most generous in this way. Ko-ishin-mit sang louder than he really needed to. His voice was never sweet, at its best. Son of Eagle heard him from far off.

"Ho, Ko-ishin-mit! Where are you going so early in the day? Come in for awhile and warm yourself by the fire," called the Eagle in a clear, strong voice. Son of Eagle was a big person and very handsome.

The greedy Raven came hopping in as fast as politeness permitted. "Choo, choo, choo. All right, all right," he said in his most cordial manner, "Choo, choo, choo."

"Sit down and warm yourself," said Son of Eagle, "while I go out and get us our breakfast." He put on his great wings and flew with the greatest of ease to the tall, tall tree.

Ko-ishin-mit watched out of the corners of his beady little black eyes. "I can fly too," he boasted under his breath.

Once on the top of the tall, tall tree Son of Eagle could see for a very great distance. Indeed, he had the sharpest eyes in all the land. He had such sharp eyes that he could spy the smallest fin of a salmon break the surface of the waters. A fat sockeye salmon dimpled the calm surface of the pool for a breath of air. He nosed up very slowly and most quietly. On his descent into the pool a tiny part of his small fin showed for a split second.

"Seek, seek, seek," sang Son of Eagle as he sailed down from his tall, tall tree and with his great talons he picked up the salmon, and in one graceful swoop he circled the wide area of the pool and sailed back to his house. All the while the beautiful, silvery salmon was wiggling helplessly in his strong talons.

Ko-ishin-mit watched and pretended not to be interested. "I can sail in the air too," he boasted to himself.

Mamma Eagle roasted the salmon over the hot, live coals she had already prepared for it. Mamma Eagle was very good at roasting salmon. It smelled so good Ko-ishin-mit dribbled and slobbered in his greed. The sweet aroma of roasting salmon wafted into his big nose. He shifted around with impatience and hunger. At last the salmon was cooked. Mamma Eagle set it on a huge wooden platter and placed it before Ko-ishin-mit.

"Slurrrp, slurrrp," the greedy Raven did not wait for his hosts to sit down with him. He gobbled and choked down the delicious, fresh roasted salmon. Ko-ishin-mit was greedy. He ate all the salmon himself. He ate so much that he fell asleep beside the open fire. The good Eagles let him sleep undisturbed.

Ko-ishin-mit awoke with a start. He roused himself and meekly murmured that he should be going home. He shook himself and the white dust of the fly-ash from the fire clouded off his coat. Thanking the Eagles he set out for his own home. If he was greedy, and sometimes ill-mannered, he was always thankful for his free meals.

Very early the next day, Ko-ishin-mit summoned his little wife.

"Pash-hook," he commanded in his most important but croaky voice, "I want you to go over to the Eagles' place of abode and say to them that I, Ko-ishin-mit, do invite them both to be my guests of honour at noon. Go now before you forget." He felt very important indeed.

Pash-hook knew well that they had no food in the house, but she went anyway without question. She always did what her husband asked of her cheerfully. She was always obedient to her husband.

It was Mamma Eagle who greeted her when she finally came to their home. "Pash-hook!" she exclaimed. "It is Pash-hook. Come in. Come in," she invited with delight. "Do tell me what you may be doing so far away from your home," she asked politely.

Pash-hook would not go in. Instead she looked over to where Son of Eagle was sitting and very solemnly announced in her tiny voice, "Ko-ishin-mit invites you — Son of Eagle — and your mate — to be — his guests of honour — at noon — today." Little Pash-hook was so nervous that she almost sang her message in one breath.

Son of Eagle looked over to where his mate was before he answered, "We shall be honoured to be your husband's guests at noon today."

"Now Pash-hook do come in and have a little bite to eat before you start back for your home," Mamma Eagle's kindly voice persuaded. "You must wait for us and we shall accompany you," she added after she had looked over at her husband.

When they arrived at Ko-ishin-mit's little abode the other guests were arriving. Soon the small house was completely filled. Ko-ishin-mit was very gracious indeed. "To the end of the room. To the end of the room," he repeated as the Eagles entered. As the other guests arrived he bade them sit according to the way they arrived. "Sit down while I go and catch a salmon," he said with gusto as he flitted and fumbled with his wings.

Ko-ishin-mit hopped and flitted, and finally away he flew. Up to a tree he flew. He sat on a dead limb of a half-dead tree that stood beside his little house. He sat there — and sat — and nothing happened. He strained his weak, little beady eyes to espy a salmon. The glare from the noonday sun on the water hurt his eyes — and still nothing.

"I must get a salmon. I must get me a salmon," Ko-ishin-mit murmured desperatley.

The noonday sun was hot. His poor eyes were tired. Ko-ishin-mit had a wonderful sense of smell, but his eyesight was very, very weak. While he perched on the dead limb many sockeye had passed by, but of course he had seen none of them.

Then, in the middle of the pool there was a ripple. It remained in the same spot. It grew bigger, and bigger still, until it was a strong disturbance in the otherwise placid pool. It made an especially big splash and Ko-ishin-mit finally saw it.

"Kootch, kootch, kootch." He plummeted like a stone. His wings were folded tightly to his sides. He hurled himself downwards, and then — Wham — his beak hit the disturbance in the middle of the pool.

Flap, flap, flap. Ko-ishin-mit was floating downstream. His wings were weakly flapping, flopping, slopping upon the surface. Flop, flop, flap.

"Ahhhhhhh," cried the womenfolk. "Ko-ishin-mit has done it again."

"Tu-shack? What has happened? He's floating down the river. Someone save him. Someone get him," cried the older men.

Strong Son of Eagle sailed out gracefully and picked up the unfortunate young Raven and carried him in his strong talons. Pash-hook put him to bed.

The tide in the river had receded during Ko-ishin-mit's watch and a big rock had pushed its hard nose above the surface of the water, and the increasing current had caused the disturbance that the weak-eyed Raven thought to be a big fat sockey. Ko-ishin-mit had hit his nose so hard against the big rock that it swelled and swelled until it was a very big nose indeed.

The Eagles returned to their home without a meal.

The old men of the village chuckled. It is not good to copy other people.

In the spring of the year, when the swallows skim
Upon the surface of the river calm,
It is time for the Hissit to ascend
The rivers and streams, fed by the lake.
On the tall, tall tree, near the sea
Sits Tzith-wa-tin the eagle strong
To sing, Seek, Seek, Seek, as he sails with grace
To snatch in his talons strong a Hissit for his mate.

Pash-hook

Ko-ishin-mit and the Shadow People

"Finders Keepers - Losers Weepers."

Most of you, no doubt, have heard this old saying. To the non-Indian way of life it means that if anyone finds anything it is his to keep, while the one who has lost it may as well cry because it is lost to him, even though someone may have found it. This did not apply to the Indian way of life.

Ko-ishin-mit, the Son of Raven, was a very selfish and greedy person. He was always longing to own other people's possessions and coveted everything that was not his. Oh, he was greedy!

One fine day, early in the spring of the year, when the sun was shining and smiling with warmth, Ko-ishin-mit overheard a group of menfolk talking about a strange place where you could see everything you could think of lying about, with never a person in sight.

"What kind of things? Where is this place? How far is it from here?" Ko-ishin-mit demanded in a high state of excitement. He was hopping up and down and his voice became croaky as he kept asking where to find the place.

The menfolk ignored his frantic questions and the speaker, a grey-haired, wizened old man, kept on with his story.

"There are canoes," he told, "big ones and small ones, paddles, fishing gear, tools, all sorts of play things and food galore. Oh, there is lots and lots of food, and the food is always fresh, even though no one is ever seen in the place."

Ko-ishin-mit became more and more excited and his voice was raspy as he screamed, "Who owns all these things? Where? How can I find them?"

The storyteller continued with his tale. "It is said that this strange place is on a little isle around the point and across the bay. The secret is that one must get there by sundown, and one must leave before sun-up. It is said, too, that the first person who finds this place may keep everything."

Ko-ishin-mit ran all the way home. "I must find this strange place first," he kept repeating to himself. "I must find the place first. I must. I must."

He flitted into his little house, and because he was out of breath he rasped and croaked, "Pash-hook, Pash-hook, Pash-hook, nah, my dear, get ready quickly. We are going out. Make some lunch. We may be gone all night," he croaked.

Pash-hook, the Daughter of Dsim-do the squirrel, scurried about. She did not need to be coaxed for she was always a fast and frisky little person. She never questioned her husband's wishes. Whatever her husband said had always been good enough for her and she was always eager to please him. So she hurried and she hurried.

Ko-ishin-mit grew more and more excited as he flitted here and hopped there inside his little house.

He got out the two paddles. He hopped down to the beach and pulled and tugged at his canoe until he had it to the water, a feat he had never before done alone.

Flitting back to the house he pressed and coaxed his little wife. "Hurry, hurry! Pash-hook, hurry! We must get there first. Hurry before we are too late. We must get there first. Oh, let us be first," he kept repeating, mostly to himself.

The sun was setting when they paddled into the bay of the little isle around the point. It was a beautiful little isle with small clumpy spreading spruce trees growing from mossy green hills. The little bay was ringed with white sandy beaches. The tide was out and the green sea-grass danced and waved at them to come ashore and rest awhile. This is what Pash-hook imagined as she eased her paddling and glided their little canoe towards the glistening beach. Pash-hook was the dreamer.

"Paddle harder! Paddle harder!" Ko-ishin-mit commanded his little wife.

Straight for the beach they glided. Ko-ishin-mit flitted out onto the wet sand. "Pull the canoe up," he ordered as he hopped up the beach, looking about to see if there was anyone else there ahead of him. He could see long rows of beautiful canoes, big and small, pulled up well above the high-water mark. They all had pretty canoe mats covering them from the heat of the day and the cool of the night. There was no one in sight. Ko-ishin-mit was hopping up the beach. He did not wait to help his small wife with their canoe.

"I got here first" I got here first!" he rasped as he hopped and flitted up to the neat row of houses on the grassy knoll that lay just below the spreading and clumpy spruce trees.

"I got here first!" the greedy Ko-ishin-mit croaked as he flitted swiftly to the biggest of the great houses. The huge door was shut and he pushed it open and hopped inside. He did not look back to see if his little wife Pash-hook was following. "I got here first," he chanted. Ko-ishin-mit, Son of Raven, was very, very greedy.

No one was to be seen. There was not a sound to be heard other than, "I got here first." Ko-ishin-mit's beady little black eyes grew even smaller in his greed to grab, grab, grab. "All is mine! All is mine!" his voice rasped out as he croaked, the way ravens do when they espy food.

"The whole village is mine. I got here first," he reasoned to himself. He hopped around the earthen floor of the great room. Big cedar boxes lined the walls. Ko-ishin-mit's greedy instinct told him that they would be full of dried and smoked food-stuffs. Indeed he did find smoked salmon, cured meats, oils, preserved fish eggs, dried herring roe, cured qwanis (camus bulbs), and dried berries.

"Everything, everything! All is mine. All is mine," he croaked as he flitted and hopped about opening boxes of oil, dried bulbs and fish-heads. Everything he saw he wanted. He wanted it all. His own drool spilled out of his mouth. He was very greedy.

Presently Pash-hook came into the great house. For the first time in her life she was not hurrying to do her husband's bidding. She did not scurry one little bit. Instead of helping her husband to carry out all the things and food-stuff down to their little canoe on the sandy beach, she slowly approached a small pile of embers that were still glowing on the centre hearth. There was no flame. The embers glowed warmly and invitingly. Pash-hook sat down and began to warm herself. She spread out her tiny hands. The embers still glowed warmly.

Ko-ishin-mit was so excited and so busy carrying out the food-stuff that he, for the first time in their married lives, forgot to make his wife do all the work.

"I shall never be hungry again. I shall never be hungry again," he kept repeating.

He worked hard packing, packing, packing, all he could lift and move down the long sloping beach. The tide was out and their little canoe was far down from the great houses. Pash-hook sat by the embers warming herself while Ko-ishin-mit worked at loading the canoe. At last the canoe was filled. It was so full there was hardly any room left for himself or for Pash-hook.

"One more trip. One more trip." How greedy Ko-ishin-mit was! He decided to put the last load where his wife would sit. He hopped up the high sloping beach and flitted into the now nearly empty cedar box and decided again he would put the very last load where Pash-hook would sit.

All of a sudden he remembered her. Pash-hook was still sitting by the fire warming herself at the embers.

"Come Pash-hook! Hurry! We must come back as fast as we can. We must take all. We must take all. We must come back before daylight returns. Hurry, hurry, Pash-hook!"

But Pash-hook still sat without moving, before the embers of the fire. Ko-ishin-mit lost his temper. He hopped to his wife's side demanding in his raspy voice, "What's the matter with you, woman? You have never disobeyed me like this before. Get up at once. We must go."

Pash-hook did not move. She did not speak. She did not look up at her husband.

Ko-ishin-mit was alarmed. he became very frightened.

"Get up, get up!" he croaked. In anger he grabbed Pash-hook by the shoulders and tried to pull her up. The harder he pulled the heavier she became. He could not budge the small little person. She felt like a rooted stone. Ko-ishin-mit was now trembling with fear. He hop-flitted out and down to his canoe and pushed and heaved trying to move it out to deeper water, but the harder he pulled and heaved the heavier the little canoe became.

"Something is wrong. Something is terribly wrong," he told himself. He tried to shout but only a weak croak came out. He flitted back to the great house and hopped inside. Pash-hook still sat by the embers of the fire.

Ko-ishin-mit noticed she was trying very hard to tell him something. He very gingerly approached her and bent his head towards her moving lips. Brave, gallant Pash-hook tried with all her might.

"There are strange people holding me down. I can't move," she whispered, almost out of breath. "Put back all you took," she entreated her husband.

Ko-ishin-mit flitted back to his canoe and once more tried to push it out into the stream. It would not move. He tried pulling it farther up onto the beach. It moved with hardly any effort at all. Trembling, Ko-ishin-mit grabbed the topmost bale and hauled it back to the great house. he worked very hard toting all the boxes and bales back to where he found them. When the last article had been returned to its own cedar box then only did Pash-hook stir.

"Heahh," she breathed, "I'm free," and shook herself and stood up. Her husband led her out and down the long, long beach to their canoe.

Pash-hook hopped in as her now very meek husband pushed the canoe into the stream. They both paddled with all their might and main until they were at a safe distance from the strange, strange place. When they at last stopped to rest Pash-hook spoke her first words since leaving the great house.

"Heahh, I'm free," she repeated. "There are people up there in the great house with the earthen floors. I'm sure of it. I felt hands, heavy hands, upon my shoulders holding me down. I'm certain that one of them sat on me because I felt so crushed down from above. I was very frightened. I couldn't speak. I couldn't tell you."

Ko-ishin-mit looked at his wife with great love. "Choo, choo, choo, all right, all right, Pash-hook my mate. Don't be afraid any more. We shall never go to that isle again."

It is said that all things belong to someone. The old people say it is not wise to keep anything you find.

Around the point and across the bay
There is an Isle with clumpy spruce
That stands on mossy knolls
Green with salal.

The beaches are covered with sea-shells white
When the tide runs out sea-grasses wave and
        beckon you in.
The shadow people live there, it is said —
Shadow people one cannot see until the sun is up
To cast their shadows on the sands of sea-shells white.

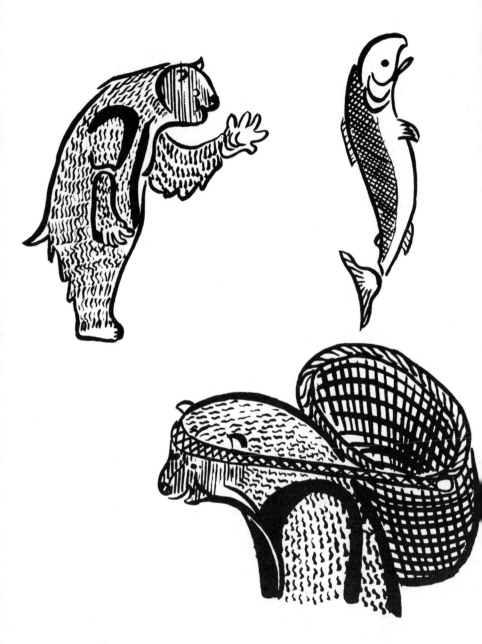

Son of Bear loved to swat salmon with his left hand.

Ko-ishin-mit Invites Chims-meet to Dinner

When Hook-sim the geese fly high in the sky,
When red leaves flutter in the gusty wind,
When chims-meet swats his salmon ashore,
Blue smoke from the alder will fill the air.
'Tis the cutting season for the folk
And the salmon will be smoked,
Done to their taste.

Red leaves sailed down the ever-increasing currents of the streams. The mist rose from the waters to meet the fresh nip in the chill of the morning air. It was late fall. The moon of the cutting and smoking season was drawing to a close.

Every household in the village was busy putting in the last of their winter's supply of dried salmon, preparing to pack it away in huge cedar food chests. Rows and rows of filleted salmon hung from the sleek cedar poles to be smoked and cured so it would keep throughout the long winter moons.

Ko-ishin-mit sat by his own little fire poking at the embers with his fire stick and wishing he could have some of the newly-smoked salmon for his next meal. He had been to every household in the village too many times, he told himself. Where could he go for his next free meal? Suddenly he thought — the bears. Chims-meet the bear. That's where he would go.

"Why didn't I think of this before," he chided himself. His excitement at the prospect of yet another free meal was overwhelming.

"Nah, my dear," he called to his little mate, "I'm going into the woods to hunt," he lied. "I may be gone for some time so do not wait to have dinner with me."

Pash-hook, his little wife, never questioned her husband's wishes and always did everything he asked of her. She loved her husband very much.

All the womenfolk in the village felt sorry for Pash-hook because they knew Ko-ishin-mit never brought any food to their house. That was the reason Pash-hook was so skinny, they all said. Normally some kind woman would find the time to bring her something good to eat but since the moon of cutting season had arrived few indeed came to offer her any food. At this time of year poor Pash-hook looked thinner than ever.

Chims-meet and Mamma Bear were big people. They were kind and thoughtful and so very generous at heart. They welcomed all people or travellers that came their way and always had a bountiful supply of food, especially during the winter moons.

Chims-meet was the best fisherman in all the land. He loved to wade into the streams when the salmon season was on. Whenever he saw Sah-tsup, the king of all salmon, he would swat it onto the beach with his great left hand. Mamma Bear would then flop it into her big cedar root basket that she carried over her plump shoulders suspended by a tump-line that ran across her broad forehead. When the basket was full of the fattest salmon she would tote it to their smokehouse, to be cut up and spread to dry on the long slender cedar poles. This was their winter food.

Mamma Bear had a heart as large as she was and always before leaving the river to smoke the salmon she would remind her husband not to catch any of the mother salmon. Indian people never molest the mother fish because they come up the streams to lay their eggs in the gravel for more and more fish to come back in other years.

During the berry season Mamma Bear would pick berries with her left hand. it is said that all bears are left handed. They do everything with their left hands. She would spread the berries on the hot rocks in the sun and when they were thoroughly cured she would store them away. At that time of year Chims-meet loved to go out and look for wild honey which Mamma bear would store in airtight salmon bladders.

The house where the Bears lived was built beside a stream where the cohoe and chum salmon went up to spawn. It was deep inside the heart of the woods a long distance from the village but Ko-ishin-mit did not mind the long walk. He was so greedy he would go any distance for a free meal.

"Well, well, well, Son of Raven. The weather is fine. Come in, come in," invited Chims-meet when Ko-ishin-mit arrived at the door of his house. "Sit down, do sit down and we shall have a bite to eat," the friendly Chims-meet said in his great rumbling voice. Chims-meet was at home because his work was done and all his food-stuff for the winter was carefully packed away in the big cedar chests.

Ko-ishin-mit saw the great boxes lined along the walls and he knew that they were filled with dried salmon, berries and wild honey. His mouth slobbered at the thought of that bounteous supply of food.

"I wonder where he keeps his oils," he thought, for no matter how much food was offered to him he always wanted more. Ko-ishin-mit was never content. He was shamefully greedy. "Best of all, I would like some oil with my broiled salmon," he kept saying to himself.

Ko-ishin-mit had not visited the Bears before and he was a little shy at first. "Ah yes, it is indeed a fine morning. I have been out hunting. The weather is too still and the creeping things are wary."

The sly one pretended not to be too anxious to stay, but all the while his beady little eyes were busy looking around the huge room for any sign of the oils he loved so well. He pretended to be very tired and he sighed and stumbled a little as he finally said he would stay for a short while.

Mamma Bear came into the room with a big fat salmon in her left hand. She stoked up the live coals and began roasting the large fish. The aroma of the salmon cooking smelled very sweet to the greedy Ko-ishin-mit.

"I wish I could have some oil with my salmon. I wonder where they keep their oils," Ko-ishin-mit kept asking himself.

At last the smoked salmon was ready. Mamma Bear wrapped it in some cedar matting and put it to steam for a while and then reached for two of the largest clam shells Ko-ishin-mit had ever seen. Setting the shells down by the hot coals Mamma Bear called to her mate, "There you are. All ready for you."

Big fat Chims-meet chuckled at his wife and then turned to Ko-ishin-mit, "Sit away from the fire while I draw the oil," and so saying he faced the live coals and spread his great hands directly over the two clam shells, all the while chanting a little rhyme:

Clear oil run smooth, good oil flow well, rich oil come now
Fill ah-meek, both ah-meek I say
Clear oil run smooth, good oil flow well, rich oil come now
Fill ah-meek, both ah-meek I say.

Chims-meet sang his ditty in a low, rich powerful voice and before Ko-ishin-mit's very eyes the clearest and richest oil began to flow from the bear's hands into the two waiting clam shells. Soon both shells were full to the brim.

"Tu-shack, tu-shack? What has happened?" was all Ko-ishin-mit could say. "Tu-shack, tu-shack?" His beady little eyes almost popped out of their sockets with surprise. Ko-ishin-mit had seen a lot of strange things in his lifetime but this was something new to him.

As was his habit Ko-ishin-mit ate with no regard to his hosts. He gobbled up the roast salmon with greed, pushing his whole hand into the oil and into his mouth without stopping. He had no manners whatever when he was eating.

Mamma Bear watched secretly as Ko-ishin-mit made a glutton of himself, since it was not polite to watch another person eating. "Oh, how the poor man can eat," she thought to herself.

As usual Ko-ishin-mit ate too much and got too full. As a result he went to sleep beside the fire and snored and snored. The good Bears kept quiet and let him sleep. At long last he roused himself and mumbled that he must be getting home. While he was dusting the white fly-ash off his coat he very politely asked the Bears to have lunch with him and his little mate, Pash-hook, the very next day.

"We shall be delighted and honoured to have lunch with you," Chims-meet replied.

When the Bears arrived on the following day, Ko-ishin-mit was very excited. He hopped and flitted about his little house ordering Pash-hook about. "Bring in more wood. Stoke the fire. Make ready the salmon for the coals. Get out my clam shell, no, make it two."

Poor little Pash-hook was agitated because of their very important guests. She was determined to please them. She scurried and bounded about doing everything her husband asked of her. She brought out their only dried salmon and then burned it by trying to roast it too near the red hot coals. She wondered what her husband wanted the clam shells for, but she got them anyway. It was said Pash-hook was light-minded but she was a good and obedient wife to Ko-ishin-mit and that was really all that mattered to both of them.

"Stand aside while I draw the oil," Ko-ishin-mit announced with a great flourish as he went up to the freshly-stoked fire clutching the glistening ah-meek. "Stand aside while I draw the oil," he repeated as loud as he could in his croaky voice.

Pash-hook's whole married life had been spent in wondering and marvelling at her husband's continual attempts, no matter how fruitless, to do anything and everything as well as any other person. Wishing above all to please her guests and her husband she poked at the fire again with the fire stick.

Ko-ishin-mit strutted to the flaming fire and squatted on his little backside. With a flourish he very deliberately spread his scrawny little hands before the hot fire directly above the waiting clam shells. He sat for several minutes before the roaring fire with hands outspread, but nothing happened.

He sat before the fire for a very long time, but still nothing happened. No oil flowed into the two clam shells. Ko-ishin-mit sat there until his whole little body was burned black — his beak, his eyes, his whole coat and especially his scrawny little hands. They were burned until they curled up into claws.

It is said by the old people that this is why all ravens, to this day, are all black, because Ko-ishin-mit, the Son of Raven, burned himself while trying to copy the fat Chims-meet in drawing oil from his hands.

The guests all agreed it was not good to try to copy other people. Chims-meet and Mamma Bear went back home without any dinner.

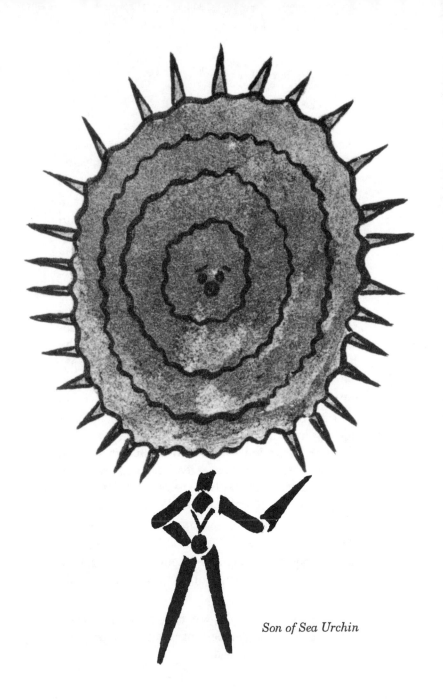

Son of Sea Urchin

Ko-ishin-mit Takes a Partner

It was a fine sunny morning. Ko-ishin-mit was out as usual, his keen nose sniffing for a possible source of a free meal. He had a very sharp, keen sense of smell. He could detect the smell of cooking from a great distance and he could go straight to the source of the cooking aroma.

Son of Shag and Son of Saw-bill were sunning themselves in front of the village when Ko-ishin-mit came ambling along with his nose in the air. He was following the smell of cooking salmon that had drifted down on the morning breeze. He could hear the two men talking. They seemed to be discussing something of grave importance because they were speaking earnestly. Suddenly Ko-ishin-mit heard his own name mentioned and he slackened his pace and listened more intently.

"Son of Saw-bill listen to me. It is a shame that a man of such noble birth, a man of such distinction, a man so important, should go about without a man-servant and bodyguard. All men of high birth should have servants. I say that Ko-ishin-mit should, by his own rights as a man of noble birth, appoint a man-servant and bodyguard right now. It is beneath his dignity to go about without a man-servant." Son of Shag spoke loud enough so that Ko-ishin-mit would hear every word that he said. Both men knew how conceited the Son of Raven was.

Ko-ishin-mit did not stop to hear more, instead he quickened his pace. The two plotters saw Ko-ishin-mit strut more proudly. He raised his nose higher. he stopped following the aroma of cooking salmon.

"Look now, Son of Saw-bill, the greedy one is actually passing up a meal. He's up to something. He heard every word said about him. Ko-ishin-mit likes his free meals too well to pass one up. He's thinking of something better than a meal for himself, you can rely on that," Son of Shag declared. Both men chuckled with glee as Ko-ishin-mit hurried past all the houses.

Ko-ishin-mit was thinking. He was a crafty, cunning person. He had always boasted that he could think for himself and this was one of the times, he boasted to himself, as he hurried back to his little house.

"If I have a man-servant he would have to go with me on my social calls and my host would have to feed him also. This would mean I would have that much less to eat. That would never do. On the other hand, as the wise Son of Shag has stated, it is beneath my dignity as one of noble birth to go without a man-servant. Yes, I must get a man-servant — but one that doesn't eat too much I think," he mused.

The tide was out. The slender sea-grass and the delicate seaweed waved and beckoned in the shallow pools along the seashore. A tiny little house stood on the very edge of the sea just above high-water mark. It was a very pretty little house and Ko-ishin-mit approached it with a deliberate step.

He did not hurry, neither did he tarry. Straight to the little house he went.

As he drew near, the smallest person imaginable appeared in the little doorway. He was obviously a happy little man for his red, rotund cheeks were wreathed in smiles. He was the Son of Sea Urchin, a member of the smallest people in the world.

"Come in, Ko-ishin-mit. May I offer you a nice feed of dried seaweed?" he chortled in his weak little voice.

Ko-ishin-mit did not like dried seaweed, but he could not resist an offer of free food so he ate it. Ko-ishin-mit was always polite so he thanked Son of Sea Urchin for the seaweed.

"Hear me now, Son of Sea Urchin. I, Son of Raven, have come to offer you a great honour," he stated slowly and deliberately. "I have given this much thought and this day, Son of Sea Urchin, I have chosen you to be my companion and partner. Your duties will be light. You will be required to accompany me on my social calls. Now know this. It will be a great honour to you. Until now I have not permitted anyone to associate with my personage. What say you, Son of Sea Urchin, will you consent to be my partner?" The proud young Raven spoke in a loud, commanding voice. He was at his very most arrogant self.

The little man thought the offer over for a short time and then he answered, "Son of Raven, I shall be very happy to be your companion. Yes, I shall be your partner," he said in his very small voice.

On their first social call they were served fresh
salmon roasted over an open fire. Each was given an
equal helping of the delicious food and Ko-ishin-
mit, as was his wont, gulped his portion down as
quickly as he could, so he could perhaps have more.
Son of Sea Urchin placed a small piece in his tiny
mouth and began to chew it, taking much time and
showing good manners. The Raven ogled his companion's share of the food with greedy, bulging eyes.

"Nah, my partner, you have far too much on your
platter. Remember you are a very small person," Ko-
ishin-mit pointed out. "Indeed I shall be very happy
to help you eat some of your share," he slyly whee-
dled. Before the tiny man could reply, greedy Ko-
ishin-mit reached across and began gobbling his
partner's dinner. He ate and he ate, in fact he ate so
much that he became ill and had to be carried to his
home.

It was a strange procession. They had put the
Raven on a cedar slab and the host had taken the
head of the stretcher while the tiny Son of Sea
Urchin did his best to hold up the foot of the wide
board. The weight of the bloated Ko-ishin-mit was
far too much for the little man and he began to
choke on the very first mouthful he had been able to
get before the Raven had grabbed his food. At last,
they managed to get the bloated Ko-ishin-mit to
his home where long-suffering Pash-hook took
charge and put him to bed.

Ko-ishin-mit opened his beady little eyes and the
very first thing he saw was his man-servant still

chewing on the first mouthful of salmon. He propped himself on his elbow and groaned.

"Do not be such a glutton, Son of Sea Urchin," he roared, "shame on you. You are still eating. The next time I take you out on my social calls I shall have to take all your share."

A tiny small person was the Son of Sea Urchin,
His wants were few because he was so small,
A bit of dried seaweed,
A wisp of slender sea-grass
Would fill his tiny mouth.
A happy little man was he
With red and rotund cheeks.
The sly cunning Raven knew of all this
So he chose him
To be his man-servant.

Ko-ishin-mit

Ah-tush-mit is Gobbled Up

Ah-tush-mit was the very first boy deer there ever was. He was a happy little boy with big eyes, long long ears and skinny legs. He loved to play all the day long because he was a happy little Ah-tush-mit.

To Ko-ishin-mit, the greedy one, he looked like something good to eat. Ko-ishin-mit was always hungry and always looking for a chance to lure the fat little deer into the woods to gobble him up.

"Come, Ah-tush-mit, let us play in the woods," the crafty Raven would coax.

"No. My mother says I'm never to go in the woods without her."

But the wicked Raven never gave up and would go off into the woods alone to think of some way to fool Ah-tush-mit.

One day Ko-ishin-mit came running to where the boy deer was playing on the sandy beach. When he got his breath back he said excitedly, "I've discovered a new game."

"A game! I know lots of games," countered Ah-tush-mit. He wasn't going to be fooled by the crafty Son of Raven who was always so full of tricks.

"But this is a new game. No one knows it except me," the sly young Raven whispered, looking around to make sure no one else was there. "I wouldn't tell this to anyone but you, because you're my very best friend and because I trust you."

"Well then, tell me." Ah-tush-mit was still suspicious.

"Shhh, not so loud. Remember this is a secret," the Raven whispered and looked all around again. "Let us go up to the bluff so that no one can overhear us. This will be our secret. No one else must share it."

Ah-tush-mit stood still but he was getting curious.

"No, my mother says..."

"But that isn't the woods. Up there on the bluff you can see the whole village. Come on, your mother will never know. I'll show you the game up there. Come on," the wily Raven coaxed and coaxed. "Remember I'm only telling you my secret because you are my very best friend."

"Well...all right then, but only for a little while...just only for a very little while."

Ko-ishin-mit hopped and flapped his way up to the high bluff with Ah-tush-mit trotting close behind. They could see the whole village below just as Ko-ishin-mit had said so Ah-tush-mit felt a lot safer.

"All right, show me your new game," he said boldly.

"It's a new, new game that no one has ever played before. It's called the crying game."

"Crying game! I don't want to cry. I'm happy. I couldn't cry if I tried." Ah-tush-mit was right. He was always happy, always romping and hopping about the sandy beach.

The sly Raven paid no attention to what the boy was saying and went on seriously. "You pretend to cry over your old, old grandparents who have been dead and gone for a long, long time," he whispered, looking very sad indeed.

"I never saw my old, old grandparents — and besides crying is no fun. I want to play — not cry," said Ah-tush-mit, trying to appear bold and brave.

Ko-ishin-mit pretended not to hear. Instead he settled himself back on his tail. "You must sit like this, bend your head right back and cryyyyy. Ahhh; nuh-nuh-nik-sooooo-mit-ahhhhh. Poorrrr old, old grandparents that were." Real tears streamed down Ko-ishin-mit's face.

After a little while he stopped crying, dried his face, looked over to Ah-tush-mit and said, "Now it's your turn. It's lots of fun, honest it is. If you can't cry, just pretend, you'll soon learn."

"I, I, I don't want to cry," Ah-tush-mit was weakening. All of a sudden he wanted to cry, especially after seeing Ko-ishin-mit's tears. He sat down on his little haunches.

"No, no, no. Not there. Come over here where I am. Turn round and face me. Back up just a bit more, there. Now look up at the sky, bend your head back as far as it will go — this will be fun for you." Ko-ishin-mit was coaxing and easing Ah-tush-mit towards the high rock. The little deer looked up to the sky, lifted his face and bent his head....

The wicked, sly, crafty Raven pushed with all his might. He pushed poor Ah-tush-mit right over the high, high cliff.

Down, down, down, the fat little boy deer plummeted like a stone. Down, down, down....

"Koootchh, koootchh, koootchh," croaked the wicked young Raven, "koootchh, koootchh, koootchh." He sailed down after the little boy deer. He caught him before he hit the rocks below and gobbled him up all in one piece.

Ah-tush-mit was gone. Gobbled up.

This was the only time the greedy Raven was full. He was so full he could hardly move and he felt very sleepy. He flapped to his little house and promptly fell asleep.

In a little while he woke with a jolt. He had an awful grinding tummy-ache. "Hahhh, hahhh, hahhh! Hahhh, hahhh, ahhh!" he moaned. Neighbours heard the moaning and groaning and went in to see what was the matter with Ko-ishin-mit. "Go away, go away. I don't want to see anyone. Hahhh, hahhh, hahhh," he moaned, "hahhh, hahhh, hahhh."

Ko-ishin-mit was very sick. There was something sharp grinding and poking in his tummy.

A good neighbour ran as fast as he could to fetch the doctor. "Doctor, doctor," he yelled, "come quickly, hurry. Ko-ishin-mit is so sick."

The doctor came — a woman crow doctor. She peered into the little house but she did not go inside. Instead she began to sing.

Wah woooo wah woooo wah lawh wa lawh. H-um
    h-um.
Ooo meehss issoook Kahsoook is eeee
Mowatchmit eeeessss
Wah lawh wah lawh. H-um h-um.

Grinding, poking in his tummy
Are the spikes, the horns
Of Moo-watch-mit the small.

The crow doctor knew what had happened to poor Ah-tush-mit. With her mind she could see the past.

Moo-watch-mit is Ah-tush-mit's other name. The song told the people that Ah-tush-mit's sharp little spike horns were grinding and poking inside Ko-ishin-mit.

"Tu-shack! Wah-se-ha Ah-tush-mit? Where is Ah-tush-mit?"

"He is not here. He's not around anywhere," said everyone.

Then they guessed what had happened to the boy deer. One of the brave, strong men sprang forward and snatched Ko-ishin-mit's robes off his couch. There lay the greedy young Raven still moaning and groaning and holding onto something that was poking his tummy out of shape.

The people knew this must be Ah-tush-mit's little spikes grinding and poking. The men dragged the Raven out of his house and cut him open to free the little boy deer.

Poor little Ah-tush-mit was still alive when the strong men pulled him out, but he was very scared.

"I'll never, never believe Ko-ishin-mit again," Ah-tush-mit promised his mother, "Or anybody — if they ask me to go to the bluffs — or anywhere. Honest. Honest."

It was Ko-ishin-mit's greed that got him into all his troubles.

To this day, it is said that crows can see into the future and into the past. When the hunters and fishermen are out and have had a successful trip the crows come to a dwelling and begin to sing to let the people know there will soon be carving and cutting.

"Wahwoooo wahwoooo wah lawh wah. H-um. H-um."

Whenever you hear the crow's little carving song sharpen your slicing knives. There is meat coming.

Son of Snipe

Raven and Snipe

In the Fall of the year, salmon up the river goes
To leave its precious roe beneath the sand and stone.
There too the wily little snipe the waters will explore
Beside the creeks and beneath the waters he will dance
To gather and store for his winter's use
The roe the salmon left beneath the sand and stone.

Son of Raven, the greedy one, loved to watch the tiny water snipe flit, hop and dance along the salmon creeks in the autumn when the fish arrive to plant their eggs beneath the gravel and stone. He would sit beneath the alder tree that grew so close to the waters that its roots strayed out into the quiet pools.

Son of Raven would sit for hours, hardly moving, until the tiny snipe appeared out of nowhere, sometimes even from under the water. From stone to stone, over and under the water, the snipe would flit and walk in his unceasing search for salmon eggs. No one knew how Son of Snipe gathered and stored the salmon eggs, not even Son of Raven, who boasted he knew everything.

One day Son of Raven resolved to visit the snipe and get a free meal. Son of Snipe did not live very far. His tiny little house was beside the creek down near the rapids. There where the waters loved to race and leap over large boulders. The waters of the

creek sang all day long as they ran, and the wind
would send the music over the hills so the people
could also hear the beautiful melody.

As usual Son of Raven arrived at the snipe's tiny
little house just before lunch time, his usual habit
when on the scrounge for a free meal. Like many of
the people of the forest, Son of Snipe was a very polite person and he bade Son of Raven to enter.

"Sit down, sit down over there by the fire and we
shall have some salmon eggs for lunch," Son of
Snipe invited graciously.

So saying, the little snipe left the room to come in
again with a small basin of water in his tiny hands.
Sitting down by the fire he carefully washed his
tiny feet. He took such pains with his task and was
so slow about it that the greedy Raven became impatient.

"Why doesn't the little fellow go about the busi-
ness of cooking the salmon eggs?" he asked himself.
He was always greedy and impatient where eating other people's food was concerned.

After a long time, or so it seemed to the Raven, the
little snipe placed his tiny little foot into a wooden
tray. Next he took out his precious little black stone.

"Now what is he going to do next?" queried the
Raven. "I am getting so hungry. I almost wish I
hadn't bothered to come at all." But of course he
wouldn't dream of leaving because he did love
salmon eggs and particularly when someone else
had caught them and cooked them.

By and by the little snipe began to feel and massage his legs. He placed both his tiny hands just below the knee and pressed down until he eventually got down to the ankle. He repeated this motion several times when suddenly he struck the ankle a sharp blow with the wee black stone.

"I wish the little fellow would stop his clowning and get on with the cooking," the greedy Raven said to himself.

In that very instant the Raven's beady eyes almost popped out of his head for there right before his eyes he saw the reddest and freshest looking salmon eggs streaming and tumbling from the snipe's tiny, little ankle. The eggs poured into the wooden tray in a steady stream until it was full to the very top. The Raven sat there with his long, big mouth wide open in wonderment.

"So this is how the little fellow stores his salmon eggs for winter use," he reflected, but he didn't pause long in wonderment before he was begging the snipe to "Hurry, hurry, hurry, let us eat."

Mamma Snipe placed a wooden pot beside the fire, filled it with water, and her husband began to put red hot stones into it. Soon it was boiling and the fresh salmon eggs were poured into it and in a very short time they were ready to eat.

"Oh, how good it smells!" the Raven drooled. "Bring it, bring it, bring it!" He was always so impatient when he was hungry and he was hungry most of the time because he was so greedy.

At last the meal was ready and Son of Snipe bade
one of his little boys place the pot in front of Son of
Raven. As usual the Raven did not wait for his
hosts but began grabbing and gulping the food down
as fast as he could so that he could have more and
more. He had a second and then a third helping of
the delicious salmon eggs, and as was his habit he
promptly fell asleep beside the fire.

Son of Snipe and his family were good, kind people, and they let him sleep. After a long time he
awoke. He roused himself, shook the fly-ash off his
black coat, thanked his hosts, and left for his home
where he hoped his wife, Pash-hook, would have
more food ready.

The very next day Son of Raven called to his wife,
"Pash-hook, go to the Son of Snipe's house. Tell him
that I, Son of Raven, wish he and his family would
be my guests of honour and sup with me tomorrow
evening. Tell him I will serve him fresh salmon
eggs. Go now!" he commanded.

Pash-hook knew very well there were no salmon
eggs in the house but she did as she was told. She
loved her husband very much and did all he told her
to do. Pash-hook had the reputation of being light
minded, but she had a big heart and loved everyone.

The snipes arrived at the Raven house in good
time and Son of Raven bade them welcome in his
usual strident manner.

"Sit down at the upper end of the room. Sit near
the fire while I go and get the salmon eggs," he

boasted loudly. He put on his best manners as he flitted busily about his little house and pretended to be very busy indeed.

"Nah, my dear. Fetch me the basin. Bring out the biggest platter. Put the pot before the fire. Fetch in more wood. Stoke the fire," he instructed his wife.

Pash-hook went about her tasks cheerfully and did everything in a great rush and tried to please everyone.

Son of Raven began washing his feet in the basin. He washed both feet very carefully and very deliberately, making a big fuss about the ceremony. Finally he wiped both feet dry and called for the platter.

Looking about the room to draw everyone's attention he very slowly put both feet into the wooden platter. He coughed, cleared his raspy throat and called loudly to Pash-hook to bring his precious stone.

Pash-hook scurried out and reappeared with a funny looking stone. It was dark in colour, but too smoky to be called black. Making a big fuss the Raven began rubbing and massaging his skinny black legs. he slowly placed his hands below his knee and began patting and rubbing his shins. Very slowly he massaged until he had reached the ankle, then, very deliberately he raised the precious stone aloft so all could see. Then he brought the stone down with all his might and struck himself sharply on the ankle. So strongly did he strike that he was knocked completely off balance and he fell onto the dirt floor.

"Kootch, kootch, kootch," he screamed with pain. He had smashed and bruised the skin of his ankle with the stone. "Kootch, kootch, kootch," he moaned as he rolled on the floor and hopped about the room on his good leg.

No salmon eggs had tumbled out of his ankle, instead it swelled and swelled until it became a big round knob. It is said that is why all ravens have knobbly knees and ankles.

There was no food for the guests. Instead they helped poor little Pash-hook to put Son of Raven to bed and she lovingly nursed his hurt little leg. Son of Snipe, the mysterious little man, took his family home without anything to eat. Everyone smiled because Son of Raven never stopped trying to imitate other people. Pash-hook was sad because her husband was hurt.

It is not wise to copy other people.

The Stranger changes Ah-tush-mit into Moowutch the Deer

How Ah-tush-mit
Became a Deer

Whetla, whetla, whetla, ohhhh ahtumahh
Qwee qwistup-sup-cha; whetla, whetla, whetla.
Sharpen, sharpen, sharpen do I sharpen
For he who changes people, changes people, changes people
Sharpen, sharpen, sharpen.

Ah-tush-mit was very busy sharpening mussel-shell knives. He sang his little song over and over again as he worked and toiled, rubbing his mussel shells on a piece of black sandstone. He rubbed and rubbed until they were sharp as could be. Whetla, whetla, whetla, ohhhh ahtu-mah.

He was so busy that he did not notice a stranger had stopped by and sat down beside him. Qwee qwistup-sup-cha, his little song continued in the clear spring morning. Ah-tush-mit loved to sing. He made up songs when he worked and when he played.

"Ho, Ah-tush-mit. What are you doing so early in the morning?" asked the stranger. He had a pleasant yet commanding voice.

Ah-tush-mit was startled. He looked up to see a stranger, like no one he had ever seen before. He was an odd looking man. He was not really big but short and broad. He wore no moccasins on his feet which were short but very broad. Ah-tush-mit could not help but notice that both his big toes turned sharply inwards. He was indeed an odd looking man. On his face he wore a broad smile that made him look odd yet important too.

"What are you making, Ah-tush-mit?" the stranger asked again.

Ah-tush-mit was surprised, yet pleased, that the strange man should know his name. He felt very important that he must be known in other lands by people of importance, so he became reckless and without thinking replied in his most commanding voice:

"Have you not heard? Do you not know? Are you not aware it is said there is a man roaming the land who is changing people into other things called birds and also into things called animals? Did you not know?" Ah-tush-mit felt very reckless and was almost rude to the stranger.

"There is a man, an evil man, who is roaming this land..."

"Choo, all right, Ah-tush-mit, and what do you intend to do with this man should he ever come and perhaps try to change you also?" the man asked very softly.

Ah-tush-mit continued his sharpening. "What are animals?" he countered the stranger's query. But before he could get an answer he continued his song and his sharpening. "Whetla, whetla, whetla..."

Presently he became bolder, and without looking up he said, "I won't let the man change me. I like me

the way I am. I don't ever want to be anything
else."

"But suppose the man who changes people, as
your own song says, insists on changing you into
something else?" the man insisted.

"I shall be ready for him. I shall be ready for him
with these knives," Ah-tush-mit declared.

"Mmmmm," the stranger said, "they are indeed
good knives. They look very sharp too. How many
have you got?" he asked quietly.

"I have two of the sharpest and biggest knives,"
Ah-tush-mit shouted in a very rude tone.

"What did you say you would do if this man that
changes people should come here and try to change
you into something else?" the stranger asked again.

Ah-tush-mit was becoming very annoyed with
this same question and boasted loudly, "I shall fight
him. I'm not scared of him. With these sharp knives
I shall fight him."

"Mmmmmm Mmmmmm. So you are going to fight
him with your knives?"

"Yes, with these knives I shall fight him and
maybe kill him." In his excitement, and because
Ah-tush-mit really thought this strange man believed everything he was saying, this wild state-
ment had slipped out before he realized what he had
said.

"Mmmmmmm Mmmmmmm Mmmmmmm. That
is not good, Ah-tush-mit. Your speech does not befit

a boy of your age," the man said softly. "Let me see
your knives, Ah-tush-mit. Give them both to me," he
asked in a very quiet but commanding voice. He
took both mussel-shell knives in his big hands and
held them up to the sunlight. There was a broad
smile on his round face.

"Mmmm," he murmured very softly. "They would
make nice long, pretty ears for a rude and foolish
boy," he mused to himself. "Come here Ah-tush-mit
while I try these on you for size. Come here to my
side," he said in a very quiet voice.

Ah-tush-mit felt very important that this man
should be interested in his knives. He stood still
while the odd looking man placed the two mussel-
shell knives on either side of his head. The knives
were stuck straight up against his head and then he
gave an order.

"Shake your head, Ah-tush-mit. There. That looks
very pretty indeed. Give me your sandstone now."
He placed it on Ah-tush-mit's rear. Patting the stone
with his big broad hand, he stood back to survey his
handiwork.

He shook his big head. "Too black. Yes. Too black,"
he said to himself, and so saying he scooped up the
white dust left from the inner side of the mussel
shells and sprinkled it to the underside of the black
sandstone.

"There, that looks better. Indeed it's perfect," the
strange man said aloud. "Mmmmm, your mussel-
shell knives are so pretty; so black on the outside

and so white on the inside. They do make pretty ears for you. Your sandstone is so very black on the topside and so very white on the inside it will make a pretty tail for you, Ah-tush-mit. Wiggle your ears. Now, your tail. Good. Very good indeed," he nodded.

The odd looking man with toes that turned inwards was pleased with his handiwork.

"Choo, all right, go now I bid you. From now on and for ever more you shall be known as Moowutch."

Away bounded the foolish young boy, his long, long ears straight up in the air and his little black tail wig-wagging to show the gleaming white underside. Poor foolish Ah-tush-mit was changed into the animal that we know as Moowutch, the deer of the forest.

It is said that is why all deer of the forest have long black ears with the innerside white, and short black tails with the underside a gleaming white.

The old people said, too, that boys and girls should never boast, nor talk too much, especially to strangers.

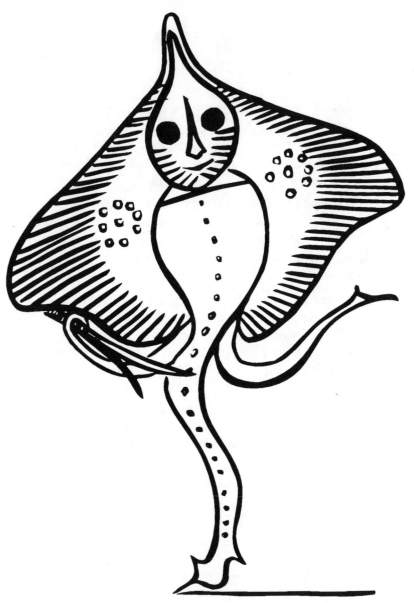

Paw-qwin-mit is so wide

Ko-ishin-mit and Paw-qwin-mit

The Moon of many Moods had come and gone.
Kloose-mit the herring had fed the children of the land
With their glistening roe they had fed the Indian people.
The last of the drying herring eggs upon the long racks
Now sun-dried to a golden hue were stored for summer use.
The Budding Moon had arrived. The time to play was
*   here again.*

It was early spring. The young men in the village vied against each other for their own clubs in tournaments, field games, wrestling matches, races, swimming, weight lifting and many more games.

Paw-qwin-mit, the Son of Skate, was the acknowledged spear-throwing champion of the whole region. It was said that he was so light and deceptive in his feints and movements that he was impossible to hit with the tournament spear. Paw-qwin-mit was a handsome young man with broad shoulders and narrow hips and slender legs.

Ko-ishin-mit, the village boaster, thought otherwise.

"He is so wide in the shoulders that you can't help but hit him, if you are strong enough," Ko-ishin-mit would boast loudly in his croaky voice. "I myself am pretty fast on my feet and I am strong. I can throw the tournament spear as straight, and as far, as anyone else," he boasted to one and all. "Paw-qwin-mit thinks he is the best now because he hasn't thrown the spear with me," Ko-ishin-mit was loud in his bragging. "I can beat Paw-qwin-mit, I know I can." He would get so excited in his boastful talk that the older men in the village would admonish him not to talk so foolishly but this would only serve to infuriate Ko-ishin-mit to louder and more boastful talk.

It was during one of these loud outbursts that he let it be known he had been training most rigidly for the spear-throwing tournament.

"I am fast on my feet. I can feint, and I am more cunning than Paw-qwin-mit." The foolish young Ko-ishin-mit had begun naming his imagined opponent.

Paw-qwin-mit was a good-natured young man. He took Ko-ishin-mit's many challenges with good humour and ignored the rude remarks thrown in his direction from the foolish and croaky voice of Ko-ishin-mit. It was known by everyone in all the region that this was one of the many qualities that made Paw-qwin-mit so popular as "The Spear Thrower." Indeed he was the undisputed champion until, of course, the foolish and boastful Ko-ishin-mit began his bragging of being the better thrower.

It was the day of the big tournament. The other sports of the field and water had been run and dealt with. At this particular time of the season when the sun was warm, when the buds on all the reawakening plants were bursting forth in their pale green crowns, and the salmonberry blossoms in their bright flaming red jackets swayed and beckoned the humming-bird small to sip nectar, when the nettle shot from the loam, the bracken unfurled its golden crown from the mossy glens and the tree-toad voiced his cracky song — then was the spear-throwing season heralded in.

The preliminaries had come and were finished. Now the senior and more experienced throwers were in the field and competing with great earnestness. The young men were many. They were all lithe, fast, strong of arm and sure of stance. The entire village was out for this event — the old, the young, the women with babies strapped on their backs or cuddled in their cradles as snug as only babies can be. This was indeed the event of the season.

Paw-qwin-mit was the chief referee of the tournament. The last bout was on and the two contestants opposed each other in earnest. Paw-qwin-mit stood to one side in the middle of the open arena. In his hand high over his head was poised a sprig of evergreen, a signal for the contestants to take their places at the ends of the open land provided for this sport. The young men paced deliberately to their respective places, ten plus two paces apart, that was the prescribed and accepted distance for the throw. The men stood clean and lithe in their fur-seal battle shorts. The men stood erect, back to back, their spear tips resting lightly on the soil directly in front of them. There was complete silence. The spring sun shone from directly overhead. These two throwers were the best, next to Paw-qwin-mit who was the undisputed champion of the entire coastal region.

"Now hear me." Both men turned slowly. "The man to my right shall throw the first spear," Paw-qwin-mit's voice was loud and clear. The contestants showed no emotion as they deliberately turned with their spears poised lightly in their strong hands.

"On your marks. Ready. Throw!"

The first spear whistled through the still air in a low, straight line. The live target deftly side-stepped and the swift shaft missed its intended mark by a scant hand. There was an audible sigh from the women of the audience.

"Throw two." The sprig of evergreen was poised overhead again.

"The man on my left will make the throw. On your marks. Ready. Throw!"

The second shaft blazed down the line chest high at a terrific speed and thudded harmlessly into the earth as the intended victim just as deftly side-stepped.

This contest was real. Each contestant was determined to win. It was certainly good enough to be next to the great Paw-qwin-mit as Thrower of the Spear. Both young men knew this and both men would surely think twice before attempting to wrest the crown from the most popular spearman of them all. Each succeeding throw seemed to come nearer to its mark but never made an actual hit. The contestants now stood face to face at all times and took their turns at the throw. It was remarkable how true the shafts sped and the speed was never diminished.

"Hear me now. Each of you have one more throw. Do you wish to rest?" Paw-qwin-mit's voice was very clear and he timed his words to come slowly as he directed his question first to one then to the other.

"No." "No." Both men declined the offer of respite.

"All right. Both men stand back to back. The man to my right will make the throw. Easy now. Turn. Ready. Throw!"

The shaft came hurtling at terrific speed towards its intended victim and again the swift missile missed its mark by a mere finger.

"The last throw. Easy. On your marks. Turn. Throw!" Paw-qwin-mit's voice was strong. It rang through the clear still spring air.

The last shaft came blazing down the line, straight for its mark it hurtled. The throng held its breath. There was no sound. This last throw would determine the outcome of the tournament. Would it find its mark?

Thud. The last and final shaft imbedded itself in the thick turf behind the broken earth of the measured arena. A full-throated cheer went up from the throng that had held its breath to bursting point, glad that neither of the young men was hit.

Paw-qwin-mit waited discreetly until the cheering had subsided to a good-natured hum before he stepped out into the arena again and his loud voice requested that the two young men step forward. In good time the two, who but a moment before were bent on hitting each other, now stood side by side

facing the great crowd. They stood very close together, almost touching. The contest was over. It was evident that there was no enmity between them, both
had broad smiles on their handsome young faces.
They stood at easy attention with their heads held
high, their eyes set well above the throng. Each had
done his utmost and each had just managed to outwit
the other. Both showed superb form. It was a good
contest. True, there were misses but one could say
that the bad throws in this contest were much too
close for the other man's comfort.

This was truly a contest of nerves. At ten plus two
paces it was almost impossible to hit an agile opponent unless fear became evident on the part of the intended victim. The thrower, too, must not at any
moment reveal any apprehension or nervousness,
however slight. It was like entering an unfamiliar village where a good watch dog comes at you snarling
and showing his fangs. Show fear and the dog will
surely charge. Stand if you must but speak to the dog
in a commanding voice. If you show no fear the creature will not attack — a simple contest of nerves.
The spear throwing then was indeed an exercise for
the nerves.

"Now hear me." Paw-qwin-mit slowly turned a complete round, as he addressed the now happy throng,
until he was facing the two men again. He touched
the right shoulder of the one, then the other, with the
evergreen sprig and in a ringing voice he declared the
contest a tie. A great shout went up from the enthu-
siastic people. It was a popular decision made by a

popular man. The two young men touched shoulders momentarily before they ran to join their companions who were still standing in the arena set aside for contestants, to be congratulated and slapped on the right shoulders good-naturedly by them all.

It was the time for any contender to step forward now and declare his challenge for the championship. The last two contestants knew better than to make such a challenge. Indeed they were very happy to be known as "Next to the great Paw-qwin-mit." According to all appearances the tournament was over. It was a successful day, there being two instead of one second best.

From the far side of the village a figure was seen approaching the field of the arena in a resolute and deliberate stride. There was a dead hush in the crowd which had been so jubilant but a moment ago. The lone figure drew nearer swiftly.

"Ko-ishin-mit!" A chorus went up from the throng, "Ko-ishin-mit! What can Ko-ishin-mit possibly be up to now?"

Ko-ishin-mit timed his appearance perfectly — the moment before the official announcement of a successful tournament. He strode directly to the centre of the arena where Paw-qwin-mit still stood and, without looking towards him, he slowly stopped his march, turned resolutely to the general direction of the Chief's and councillors' platform, and in his loudest croaky voice announced: "I, Ko-ishin-mit, do now, this day, hereby challenge the so-called spear-throw champion, Paw-qwin-mit, to a duel, here and now to determine who really is the champion."

"Tu-shack, tu-shack? What has happened?" was all the elders and councillors could muster in their complete surprise to this totally unexpected turn of events.

Ko-ishin-mit stood perfectly still after his brazen challenge. His beady little black eyes were fixed resolutely on the Elder. There was consternation within the ranks of the officials on the Chief's platform. Ko-ishin-mit readily sensed this and foolishly gloated over the awkward situation he had created, however temporary it may have been. For the moment he was master of the situation.

At long last, after a prolonged delay and confusion, the otherwise staid and venerable Elder stood up. There was complete silence in the great throng — not from awe nor from respect but from complete surprise. Ko-ishin-mit had timed his appearance perfectly. He was master of the situation and he knew it.

"What say you, Paw-qwin-mit? You have heard the challenge. Bear in mind that you are honour bound to defend your title." The wise old Elder spoke slowly and directly to the champion.

There was now an audible murmur from the official platform. "No, no, no. This cannot be. This must not happen. It is sheer foolishness."

Paw-qwin-mit recovered from his initial surprise. He reluctantly looked towards Ko-ishin-mit, hoping to see him show that he was only clowning.

The challenger stood his ground. He made no move. His eyes were still fixed on the now standing Elder. He was master of the situation. He gloated. Even then the champion spear thrower could not believe this awkward situation was real. His own eyes sought those of the Elder for some explanation. He was shaking his head very slowly, hoping now desperately that this display of utter foolishness was but a joke on the part of Ko-ishin-mit.

"The so-called champion spear hurler is scared. If he refuses to meet me then I am the real and rightful champion," said Ko-ishin-mit seriously.

Paw-qwin-mit's face was cast towards the ground in apparent consternation. This is real, he admitted to himself, this is real. He lifted his head slowly and sought some explanation from the Elder. "Tell me he jokes. Tell me this is not real," he said silently to himself. There was complete silence. The Elder refused to repeat his admonition to Paw-qwin-mit of a moment before. Doubtless, he too hoped that the foolish and impulsive Ko-ishin-mit was indeed joking. All knew without a shadow of a doubt that he would never have a chance as a spear hurler with the thus far indomitable Paw-qwin-mit.

Ko-ishin-mit's ego was increasing by the moment and he showed it to the best advantage. "Paw-qwin-mit, I shall stand here and await your return. Go and bring your best shaft. I will duel with you to the finish," Ko-ishin-mit spoke brusquely. He mistook the throng's silence as awe for his contempt for the champion, when indeed it was pity for his foolishness.

Paw-qwin-mit reluctantly left for his home and soon returned. In his hand he carried a short shaft with two protruding tips. It was a practice shaft — not the real throwing shaft.

"To your respective places. Do not turn until I give the command. Do not throw until the command is given to do so. The championship is at stake. Each of you must abide by the rules." The Elder was visibly not happy with the turn of events but he knew his duties. He carried them through.

Ko-ishin-mit strutted affectedly and with pomp to his chosen end. He had bedecked his person, which was completely black, with gleaming red feathers. Around his black head, around his elbows, his waist and his knobbly knees and ankles were festooned arrays of red feathers. He was indeed a sight to behold.

Paw-qwin-mit did not bother to change his attire or to add any frills. He came in his natural dress, without any costume whatsoever. He walked reluctantly, almost foolishly. He felt ridiculous to have to submit to this foolhardy situation perpetrated by this known foolish and senseless person called Ko-ishin-mit.

"I throw first," Ko-ishin-mit's voice was loud and croaky. "I throw first."

Paw-qwin-mit nodded in assent, otherwise he made no reply.

"On your marks. Turn. Get set. Throw!" The Elder's voice was shaky. It was evident that he was nervous, not because of the outcome of this duel but because he had permitted it to take place.

Ko-ishin-mit had plotted out his strategy in forcing this showdown, in a manner only he could carry out, with utter folly. He leaned far back, ostensibly to impel his shaft the faster. This tell-tale and unnecessary manoeuvre of course gave Paw-qwin-mit ample time to determine the type of throw that would come. He avoided the oncoming shaft with no apparent effort. Ko-ishin-mit's shaft thudded harmlessly into the earth.

"Throw two. On your marks. Turn. Throw!"

Ko-ishin-mit suddenly became animated. "Klootch, klootch, klootch." He was jumping straight up and down in an amazing exhibition of grotesque light-footed manoeuvres. "Klootch, klootch, klootch," he sang loudly in his croaky voice, "Klootch, klootch, klootch."

No doubt this was to distract and otherwise unnerve the great Paw-qwin-mit. The champion stood motionless. His cool, sure eyes followed Ko-ishin-mit's every move, hop and jump.

Zing! The two-pronged shaft seemed to come from nowhere. It whizzed through the silent air at unbelievable speed. Before any of the onlookers realized what had happened Ko-ishin-mit was pinned to the soft earth. His two knobbly black legs were clamped solidly betwixt the twin prongs of Paw-qwin-mit's practice shaft. Ko-ishin-mit flapped gallantly to free himself but without success and soon exhausted himself with his great efforts to regain his feet. There he lay, helpless, with both feet pinned to the ground.

Paw-qwin-mit trotted lightly over and freed him, helping him to his feet. A great deafening roar came from the throng. Not for the victory but for the champion's true sportmanship. This was what made him a great champion — together with his ability to turn with no apparent effort to show but a mere sliver of himself sideways. The handsome young Paw-qwin-mit was indeed broad in the shoulders. Sideways he was so thin he made a very difficult target to hit. So all he had to do to avoid the thrusts was to turn sideways. The foolish Ko-ishin-mit did not realize this till too late.

Paw-qwin-mit admonished Ko-ishin-mit never to jump or leap in the air. "Once your feet left the solid ground you were relatively helpless to any average spear hurler, and you dragged your feet under you so. You are lucky that you did not challenge any of the other more reckless young hurlers to a duel to the finish because I say that they would have finished you, and for good."

For once in his life Ko-ishin-mit was meek. He realized that he was indeed very lucky to escape with his life and only because of Paw-qwin-mit's good graces.

"You are the Champion," he murmured weakly.

To this day it is said that all Ravens hop-skip and jump whenever they move on their feet.

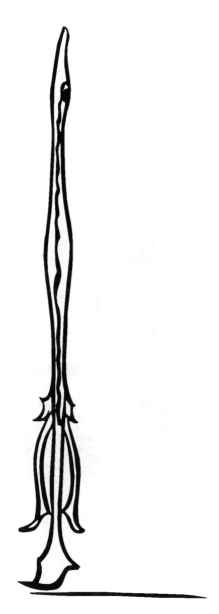

Paw-qwin-mit would turn

A lovely, lovely day to travel in

Ah-tush-mit Goes Fishing

Jig-ajig-ajig-ajig. Jig-ajig-ajig-ajig.
The cod season has come.
In the shallows by the outer isle
The codfish will come the herring to take.
Jig-ajig-ajig-ajig. Jig-ajig-ajig-ajig.
The cod season has come.

Ah-tush-mit, the Son of Deer, decided to go fishing. He gathered his gear together and made ready his hopinwush, his little dugout. He polished his little paddle until it was smooth and shiny so that it would cut the water well. He went early to bed so he would be rested and get up bright and early.

He wanted to fish for cod at the outer isle where the fish loved to lurk in the shallows, seeking the herring he would offer. The morning sun was not yet there when Ah-tush-mit arrived at the outer isle. He paddled to the best spot, and carefully choosing the best herring bait in his basket he baited his bone hook with the greatest care. Fixing the hook to the long line and a stone sinker at the proper depth, he was ready to catch cod. He was not only going to get the biggest fish, but he was going to fill his little canoe to the brim. He would sing a great song as he paddled home. There would be cod for everyone.

At-tush-mit paid out his line and when he felt the stone sinker thump on the sandy bottom he began to jig the line. Jig-ajig-ajig-ajig. He waited.

Nothing happened. He waited some more. Still nothing happened. The sun came up and smiled down on Ah-tush-mit, but no codfish came and pulled on his line. He was tired of jigging and let his line rest on the bottom. Still nothing happened.

The sun rose higher and higher. It no longer smiled on Ah-tush-mit. It was getting hotter and hotter. His legs ached from being tucked under him in his small hopinwush. No cod pulled on his line.

After a long time Ah-tush-mit looked around and saw there were big war canoes coming towards him. He watched as they came closer and closer. Then he saw it was the Wolf people — the most dreaded people in the land.

The war canoes came closer and closer and Ah-tush-mit was very frightened. Suddenly, to his relief, the canoes veered away and passed by, going very fast.

Foolishly, Ah-tush-mit then thought he would have some fun with the Wolf people. There were no cod anyway. The war canoes were a long way off now and he felt safe.

Cupping his little hands to his mouth he sang out over the calm waters, "A lovely day to travel in, great people of the Wolves." Then softly, almost but not quite under his breath, he added, "You bony, bony noses, bone-eaters all." The foolish little boy deer chuckled to himself. "Hee, hee, hee, he, he. This is fun," he thought.

The biggest canoe stopped and the leader called out, "Ho. What did you say, Ah-tush-mit?"

"I said what a lovely, calm day to travel in, great people of the Wolves," the Son of Deer sang over the waters. The Wolf people seemed satisfied so he said softly, "Bony, bony noses, bone eaters all. Hee, hee, hee, hee."

The big canoe turned about and came swishing back towards the tiny hopinwush. "We heard you, Ah-tush-mit." So saying the Wolves picked up the small canoe and placed it right in the middle of their own great craft. Ah-tush-mit sat like a carved totem. He was very frightened. He could not move. He could not speak. He was frightened out of his wits.

"Bring him along with us," the Wolf Chief growled. "He will make me a fine slave."

So the Wolf people took Ah-tush-mit for a slave because he had been cheeky to them. Wolf people have big ears and hear even a whisper. When they reached the Wolf village they put Ah-tush-mit's little hopinwush on top of the chief's great house so that he could never escape. He was now the Wolf Chief's slave.

Ah-tush-mit was a good slave. He did his work well and cheerfully. Soon all the little Wolf boys learned to love him. He sang and danced as he worked and leaped and hopped better than any of the little boys in the Wolf village.

One night the Wolf Chief commanded, "Ah-tush-mit, sing me to sleep."

Ah-tush-mit crept close to where the great Wolf Chief lay and began to sing:

Waa-itch-cha-waaa, waa-itch, waa-itch;
Waa-itch-cha-waaa, waa-itch, waa-itch.
Waa-each waa-each yooi, yooi
Waa-each waa-each yooi, yooi.

Ah-tush-mit crooned softly — sleepy, sleep, sleep. His voice was soft and whispering, soft and dreamy and the Wolf Chief became drowsy; he dozed and soon he was fast asleep. All the other Wolves slipped into slumberland too. Sleep. Sleep. Sleep. The note was soft, low, sleepy...and was gone.

The fire was burning low
All was quiet, quiet, quiet
Dying embers in the pit
Cast a spooky shadow on the wall.

In the middle of the great house the fire was dying down. The keeper of the fire had fallen asleep too. There was the sound of steady breathing all about. All was quiet — all asleep.

Like thunder, Ah-tush-mit heard his thumping heart beat against his ribs. Like an angry sea his blood rushed to his ears. Thump...thump...thump. He rolled his big eyes this way and that way, twitched one long ear, then the other. He loosened his sash and felt inside; it was there — his mussel-shell knife. His mouth and throat were dry. His knees shook. He must be brave...brave...brave.

He reached inside his tunic and pulled out his mussel-shell knife. The shell gleamed in the dim glow from the fire. He crept close to the couch of the Wolf and reaching out lifted the robe that covered the sleeping chief. He must take care. He must be brave — swishhhhhh! He had cut the Wolf's head right off.

Grabbing the head he ran out and clambered onto the roof where the Wolves had put his hopinwush. He pulled it down, carried it to the water and threw the head into the bow. Away he pushed, and paddled with all his might.

"I'm a hero. I've killed the dreaded Wolf. My mother shall have the head." All these things he boasted to himself. Then he felt weak and there was a big lump in his throat. He wanted to cry.

Ho pots yha lhahhhh, ho pots yha lhahhhh
Thoo tsee tut mooot, Qwa yhaa tseek mooot.
Moot moot, moot moot; moot moot, moot moot.

On the bow, on the bow,
The head that was, the Wolf that was
That was that was, that was that was.

It was a song for the dead. It was a lament. It was a crying song. On the bow, on the bow...Ah-tush-mit's small voice was full of grief....

Master Crane and his bag of fog.

In the meantime Mamma Wolf had awakened and found the bed was wet.

"Wake up, wake up!" she scolded her mate. "Wake up there, you have wet the couch, you shameful creature. Wake up and get yourself out of doors."

The Great Wolf Chief did not move; he made no sound. Mamma Wolf reached over to shake his head... but there was no head!

"Ahhhh! Awake, awake! Awake, awake!" screamed Mamma Wolf. "Something terrible has happened."

The great house was in a turmoil. The fire was rekindled and tall bright flames licked at the huge rafters above.

It was the Wise Old Wolf who recovered his wits first and demanded to know who was missing. The whole household was up now and scurrying about.

"Count heads!" commanded the Wise Old Wolf. "Where is Ah-tush-mit? Ah-tush-mit is not here. Find Ah-tush-mit!"

A young Wolf came bounding in to report that Ah-tush-mit's dugout was gone.

The wise one spoke again. "Ah-tush-mit must have done this to us. He is the only one missing. He must be the guilty one. Now you elders, you wise ones think. What can we do?

The young braves thought, the menfolk thought, the elders thought. Everyone was thinking what they could do.

There was a very old Wolf who slept in the far-
thest corner and he was brought forward. "What can
we do?"

"Call Ah-noos-mit, the Son of Crane," said the
very old one. "Call Ah-noos-mit, he owns the bag of
fog."

Master Crane was called and he came. He was a
big fellow and came walking slowly on his long,
long legs.

"Will you lend us your bag of fog?" asked the Wise
Old Wolf. "Ah-tush-mit has escaped in his dugout.
With the head of our chief he has gone."

Ah-noos-mit, the Crane, stood with hunched
shoulders. He was very, very tall. He blinked his
black eyes and thought for a long, long while. He
looked up to the rafters; he looked through the
smoke hole. No one spoke; no one stirred. The re-
quest was not repeated.

Ah-noos-mit was meditating. Should he give or
not?

"I will lend you my bag of fog, but you must be
very careful, very careful. Open the bag only a little
bit," his deep voice seemed to come from nowhere. "I
will lend you my bag of fog," he showed no sign of
excitement or emotion. "Be very, very careful." With
this repeated admonition he turned and walked
out on his long, long legs.

The biggest and strongest Wolves carried the bag
of fog down to the beach where the Old Wolf ordered them to let the fog out. It spilled out and out

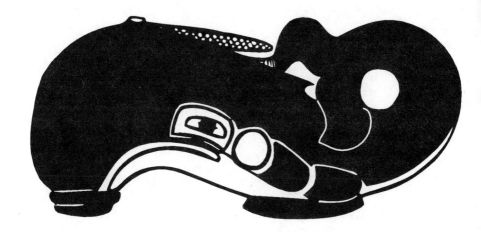

Whale design oil dish

— over the sea, onto the land, into the air. It spilled everywhere. The whole land was filled with fog, so thick the Wolves could not see each other and all were lost in the fog.

"Call the owner of the fog," commanded the Wise Old Wolf.

"Master Crane, Master Crane," they all called, "come quickly."

The Crane came and gathered the fog into his great bag.

"You must be careful, very careful. Put the fog upon the waters, let the cord loose a little bit, a little bit, careful, careful." His great voice seemed to be everywhere saying, "Careful, careful, careful."

The fog was cast upon the waters until the sea had disappeared in the great fog.

On the bow on the bow
The head that was, the wolf that was
That was that was, that was that was.

Ah-tush-mit's lament came floating in with the wind; his crying song came out of the fog. It grew louder and louder. He had got turned around in the fog. He was coming back to the Wolf village. Soon the Wolves could see the little hopinwush — could see the head of the Wolf that was.

"Be very still," whispered the wise Old Wolf as the little dugout came closer and closer.

Ah-tush-mit saw the beach ahead of him and stopped his lament, his crying song, as he beached his canoe and jumped out onto the sand.

Mother, mother here I have for youuuuu
A chamber for you I have brought.
Come, do come see this chamber that is yours.
Mother, mother here it is for youuuuu.

There was no response; no one spoke; no one moved; there was no sound. Ah-tush-mit stooped to examine the sand.

"Now!" commanded the Wise Old Wolf.

The angry Wolves sprang upon the small Son of Deer.

"Ahhhhhhh," was all Ah-tush-mit could utter as they sprang.

"Ahhh, leave, I pray, my stomach whole upon the land."

The terrible and angry Wolves gobbled up Ah-tush-mit, but, as he wished, they left upon the land his whole stomach.

It is said that is why, to this day, all wolves leave the deer's stomach whole upon the land, and that Ah-tush-mit did not really die but was born again.

West Coast Indian

In the beginning he merely marked
Then he incised on rock.
Later he carved on wood to paint and colour
        with rock and roe.
He believed in a God; he aspired to a generous heart.
Asked for strength of arm, a true aim for his bow,
To provide and share with his fellow man.

He did his work at summertime.
He waxed strong; his possessions increased with his toil.
With the thunderdrum he sang at wintertime,
Great feasts he gave because his heart was full,
He sang of deeds and glories won by his house
        and his clan.
He was at peace with his God; his life indeed was full.

He chose the timber wolf for his symbol,
The killer whale was lord of the salt-chuck,
The thunderbird meant power and might
Like the wind, rain, and the thunder.
The lightning snake was its ally.
Mah-uk, leviathan of the sea, represented abundance.

Inspired thus, on great cedar planks he drew
The symbols of his tribe.
Earth and rock, the root and bark, the salmon roe,
Lent their colours, bold and true;
Indeed great men from far off lands marvelled to see
Art forms, shown nowhere else but here.

Allied to the Nootkas, the Tse-shahts
Belonged to the clan of the wolf.
With all the powers at hand,
A great potlatch he would now command.
To bid you: "Come, enter and share with me."
A rich cultural inheritance is his indeed.

CLUTESI, Expo '67